THE PLAYLI

CW00408077

Published by
Wise Publications
8/9 Frith Street, London, W1D 3JB, England.

Exclusive distributors:
Music Sales Limited, Distribution Centre, Newmarket Road,
Bury St Edmunds, Suffolk, IP33 3YB, England.
Music Sales Pty Limited
120 Rothschild Avenue, Rosebery, NSW 2018, Australia.

Order No. AM984137   ISBN 1-84609-274-4
This book © Copyright 2005 Wise Publications,
a division of Music Sales Limited.

Edited by David Weston.
Printed in the United Kingdom.

Your Guarantee of Quality:
As publishers, we strive to produce every book
to the highest commercial standards.

The music has been freshly engraved and the book has been
carefully designed to minimise awkward page turns and to make
playing from it a real pleasure. Particular care has been given
to specifying acid-free, neutral-sized paper made from pulps
which have not been elemental chlorine bleached.

This pulp is from farmed sustainable forests and
was produced with special regard for the environment.

Throughout, the printing and binding have been planned
to ensure a sturdy, attractive publication which should give
years of enjoyment.

If your copy fails to meet our high standards, please inform us
and we will gladly replace it.

WISE PUBLICATIONS
part of The Music Sales Group
London / New York / Paris / Sydney / Copenhagen / Berlin / Madrid / Tokyo

Guitar Tablature Explained

Guitar music can be notated in three different ways: on a musical stave, in tablature, and in rhythm slashes

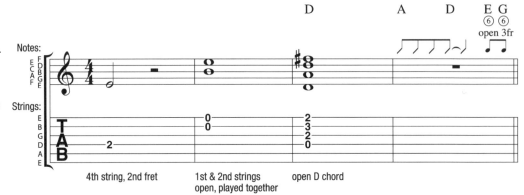

RHYTHM SLASHES are written above the stave. Strum chords in the rhythm indicated. Round noteheads indicate single notes.

THE MUSICAL STAVE shows pitches and rhythms and is divided by lines into bars. Pitches are named after the first seven letters of the alphabet.

TABLATURE graphically represents the guitar fingerboard. Each horizontal line represents a string, and each number represents a fret.

4th string, 2nd fret

1st & 2nd strings open, played together

open D chord

Definitions for special guitar notation

SEMI-TONE BEND: Strike the note and bend up a semi-tone (1/2 step).

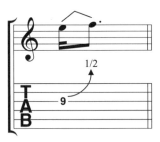

WHOLE-TONE BEND: Strike the note and bend up a whole-tone (whole step).

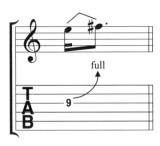

GRACE NOTE BEND: Strike the note and bend as indicated. Play the first note as quickly as possible.

QUARTER-TONE BEND: Strike the note and bend up a 1/4 step.

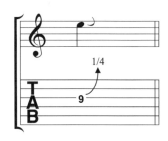

BEND & RELEASE: Strike the note and bend up as indicated, then release back to the original note.

COMPOUND BEND & RELEASE: Strike the note and bend and down in the rhythm indicated.

PRE-BEND: Bend the note as indicated, then strike it.

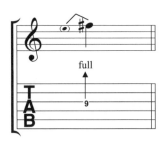

PRE-BEND & RELEASE: Bend the note as indicated. Strike it and release the note back to the original pitch.

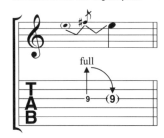

HAMMER-ON: Strike the first note with one finger, then sound the second note (on the same string) with another finger by fretting it without picking.

PULL-OFF: Place both fingers on the notes to be sounded, strike the first note and without picking, pull the finger off to sound the second note.

LEGATO SLIDE (GLISS): Strike the first note and then slide the same fret-hand finger up or down to the second note. The second note is not struck.

MUFFLED STRINGS: A percussive sound is produced by laying the fret hand across the string(s) without depressing, and striking them with the pick hand.

NATURAL HARMONIC: Strike the note while the fret-hand lightly touches the string directly over the fret indicated.

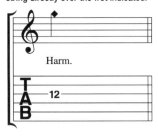

PICK SCRAPE: The edge of the pick is rubbed down (or up) the string, producing a scratchy sound.

PALM MUTING: The note is partially muted by the pick hand lightly touching the string(s) just before the bridge.

SHIFT SLIDE (GLISS & RESTRIKE): Same as legato slide, except the second note is struck.

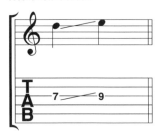

NOTE: The speed of any bend is indicated by the music notation and tempo.

Do You Want To

Words & Music by
Alexander Kapranos, Nicholas McCarthy, Robert Hardy & Paul Thomson

*chords implied by harmony

me." And now I know, now I know, now I know, I know that it's you. ___ You're luck - y,

luck - y, you're so luck - y. Doo - doo, doo, doo, doo, doo, doo - doo. Doo - doo, doo,

4

6

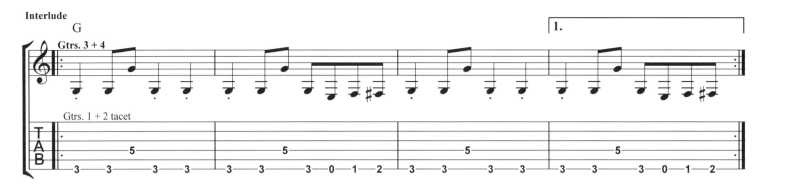

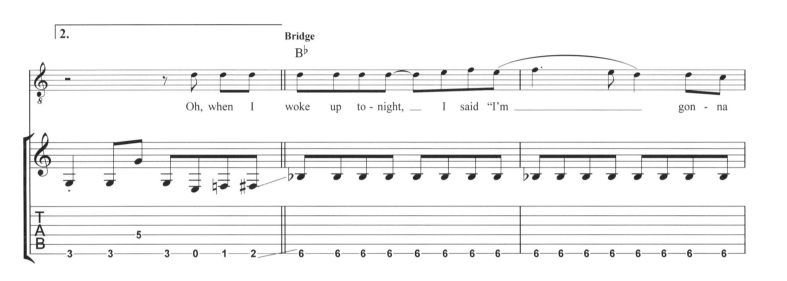

Oh, when I woke up to-night, ___ I said "I'm ___ gon - na

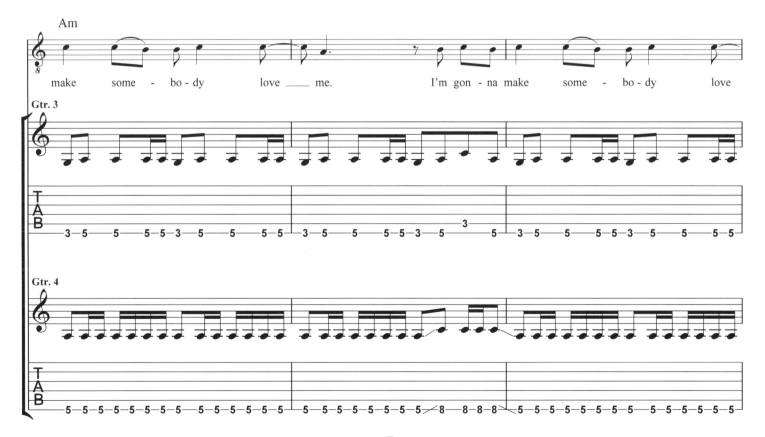

make some - bo - dy love ___ me. I'm gon - na make some - bo - dy love

—— me." And now I know, now I know, now I know, I know that it's you.

You're luck - y, luck - y, you're so luck - y.

D.S. al Coda

Coda

Gtrs. 3 + 4

Gtrs. 1 + 2 tacet

8

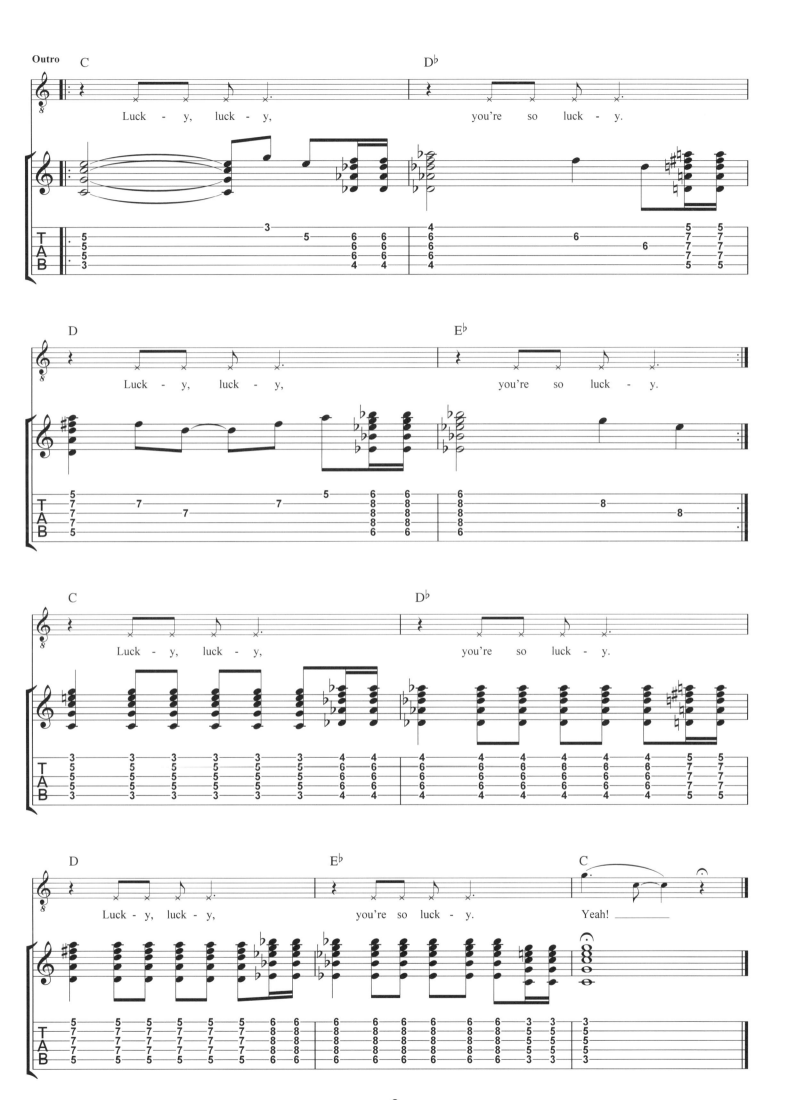

I Predict A Riot

Words & Music by
Nicholas Hodgson, Richard Wilson, Andrew White, James Rix & Nicholas Baines

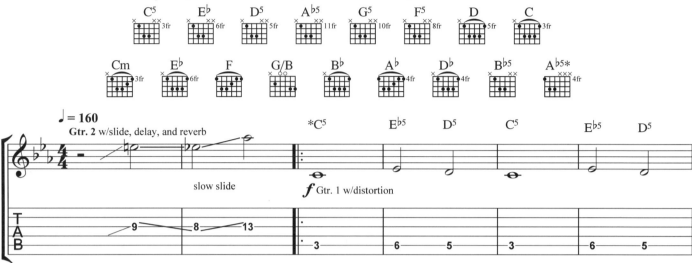

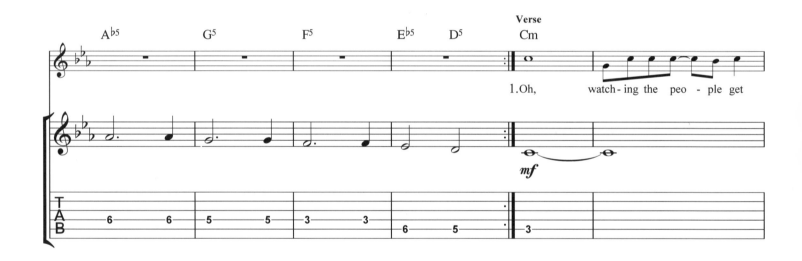

*Chords implied by harmony throughout except where indicated.

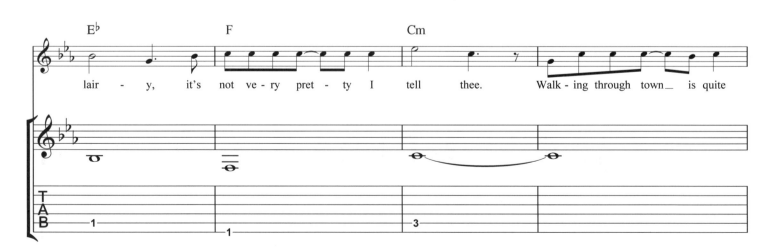

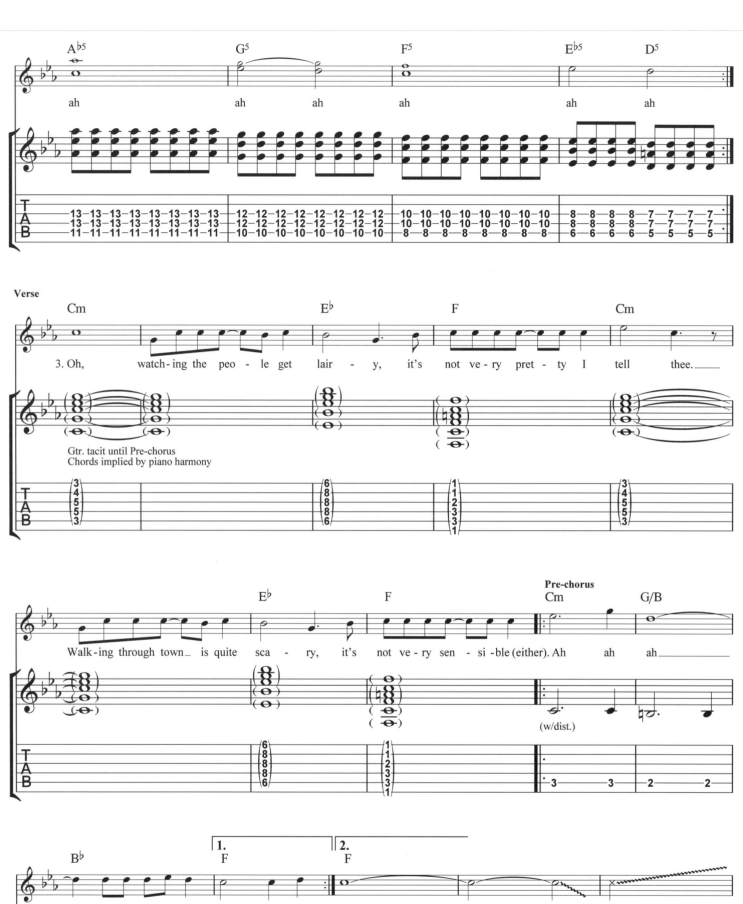

Living For The Weekend

Words & Music by
Richard Archer

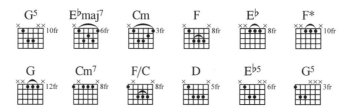

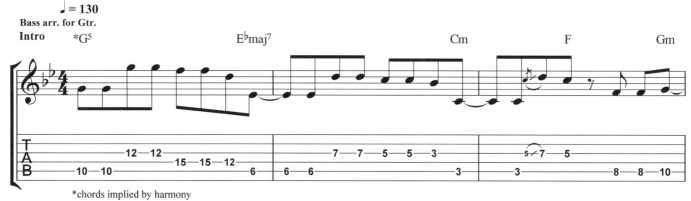

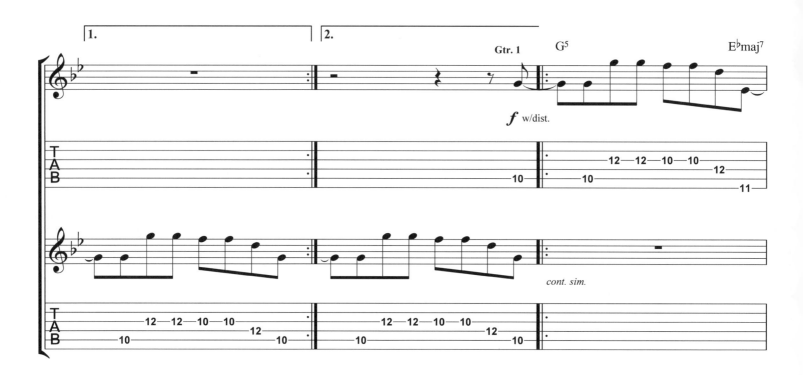

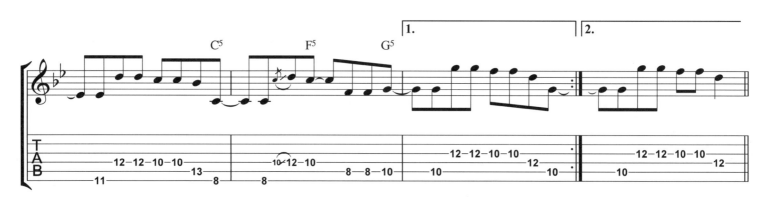

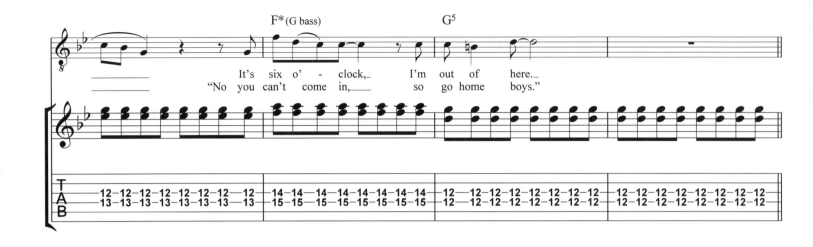

Pre-Chorus

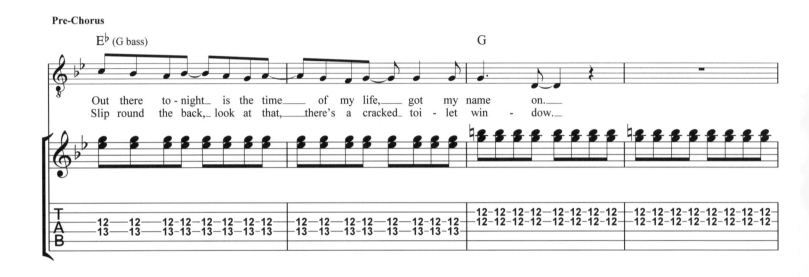

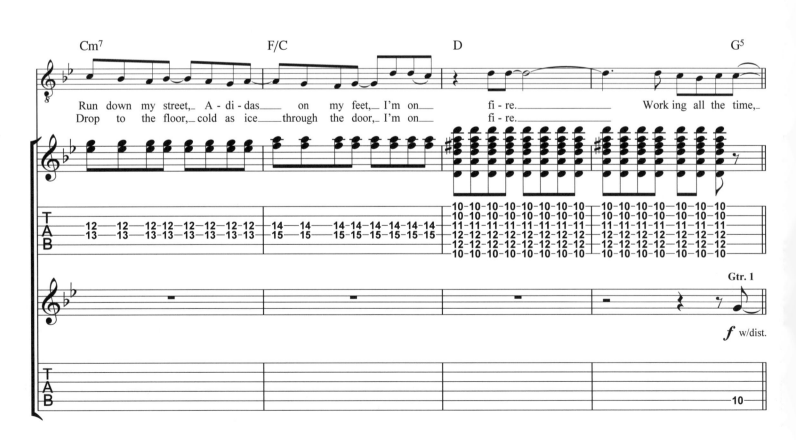

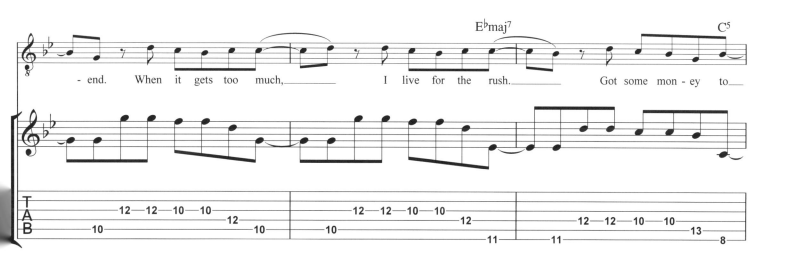

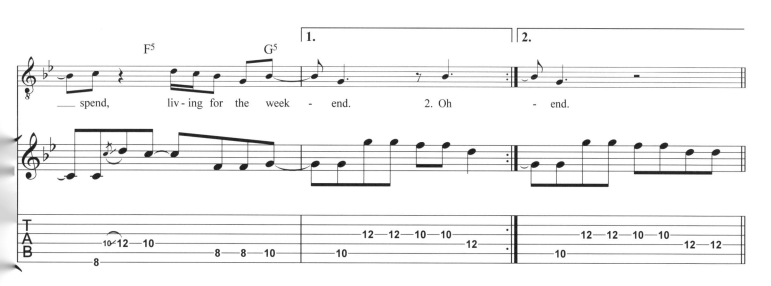

Fix You

Words & Music by
Guy Berryman, Jon Buckland, Will Champion & Chris Martin

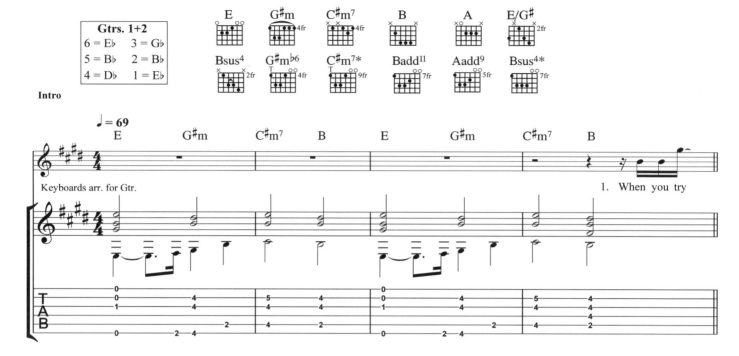

Intro

Keyboards arr. for Gtr.

1. When you try

Verse

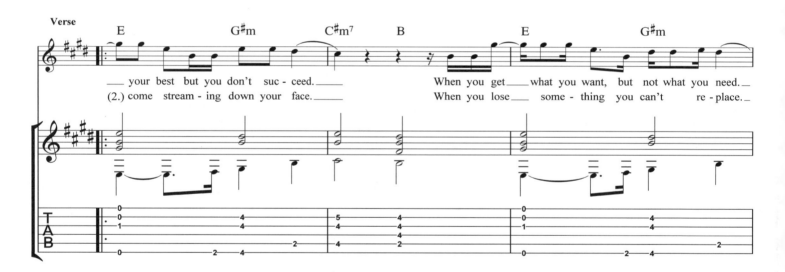

_ your best but you don't suc - ceed._ When you get _ what you want, but not what you need._
(2.) come stream - ing down your face. _ When you lose _ some - thing you can't re - place.

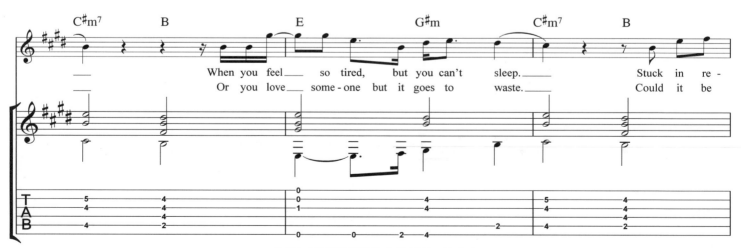

When you feel _ so tired, but you can't sleep. _ Stuck in re -
Or you love _ some - one but it goes to waste. _ Could it be

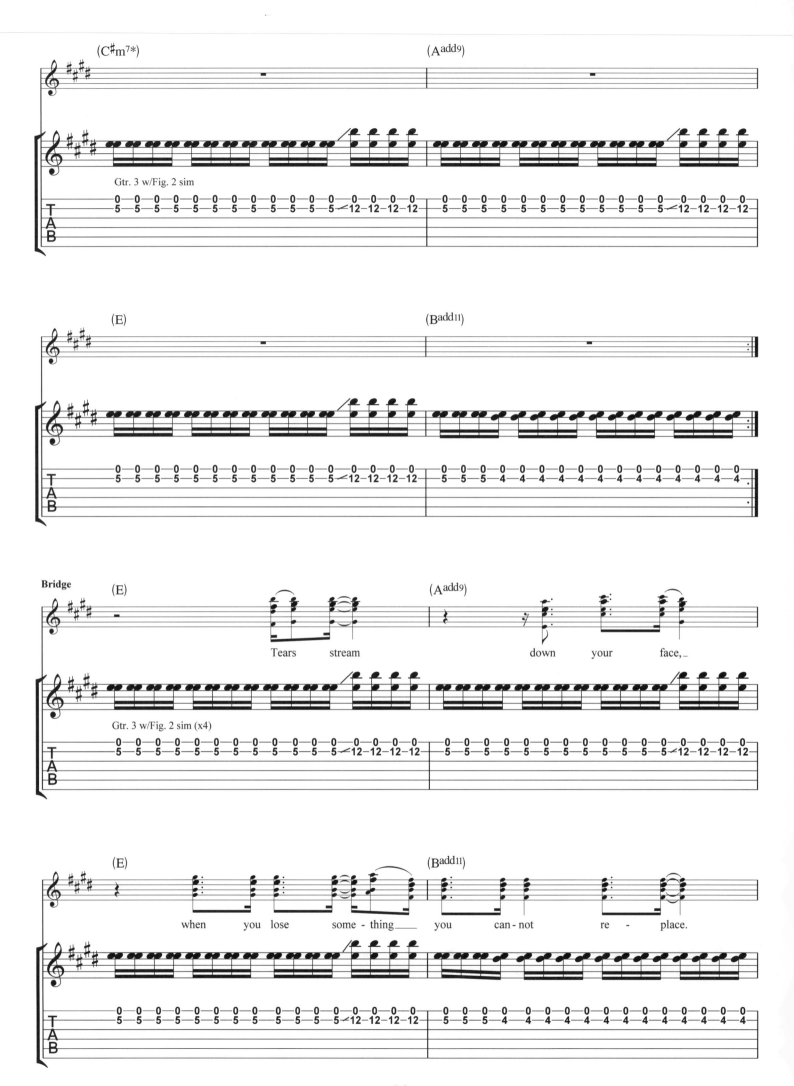

26

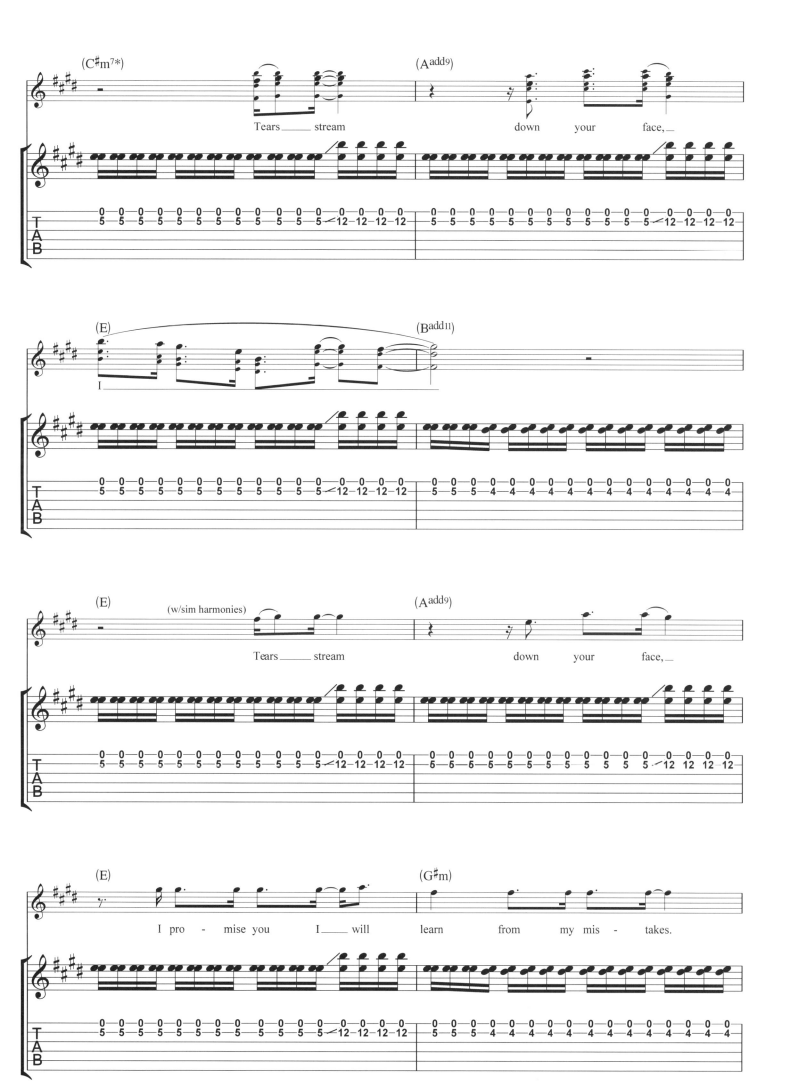

The Importance Of Being Idle

Words & Music by
Noel Gallagher

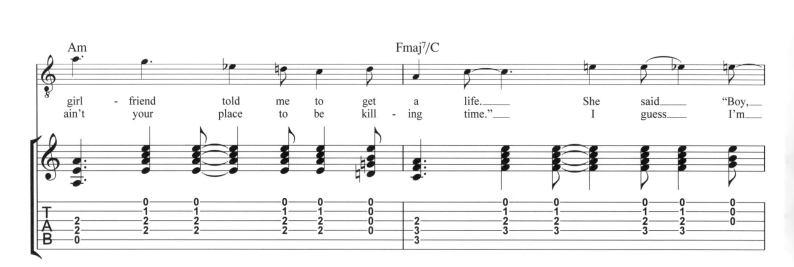

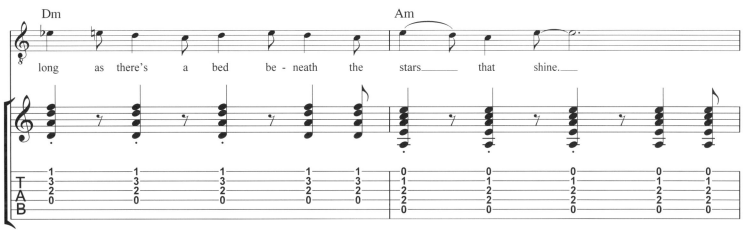

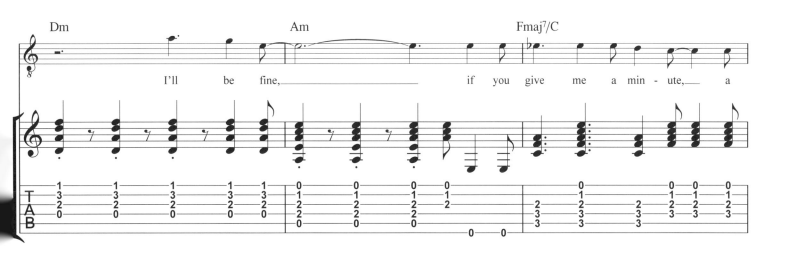

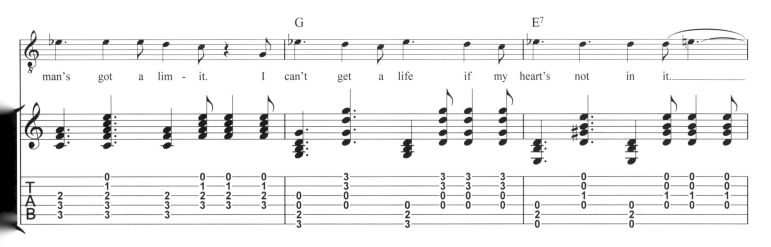

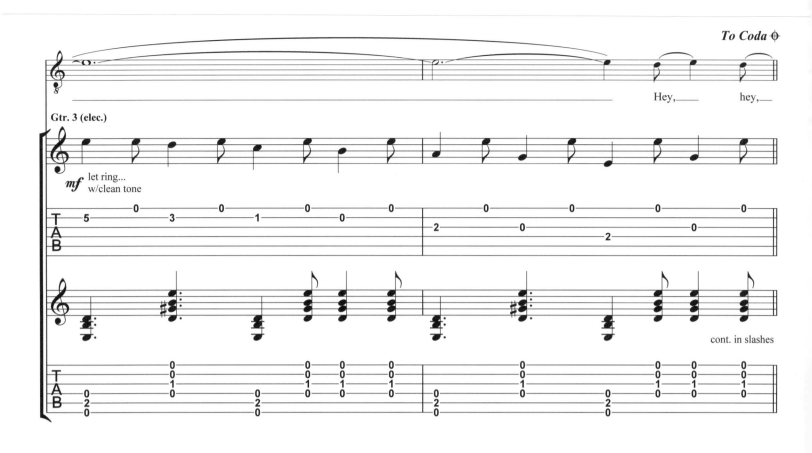

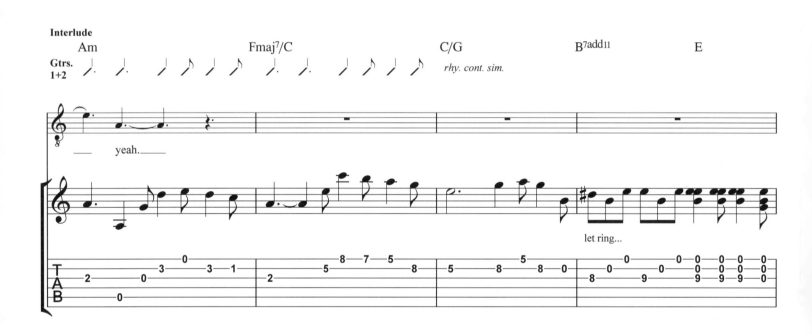

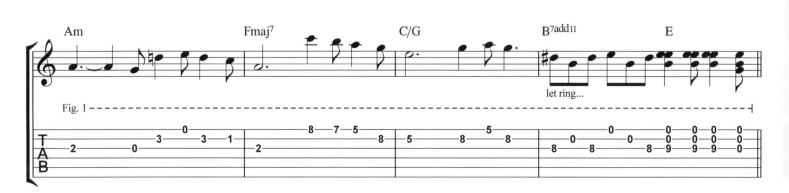

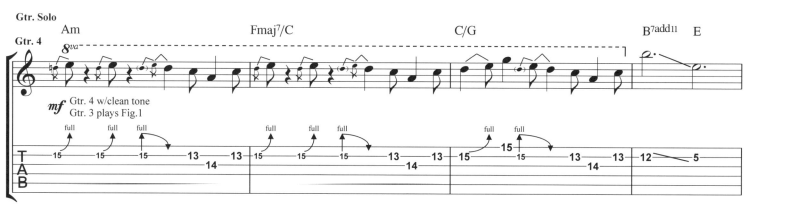

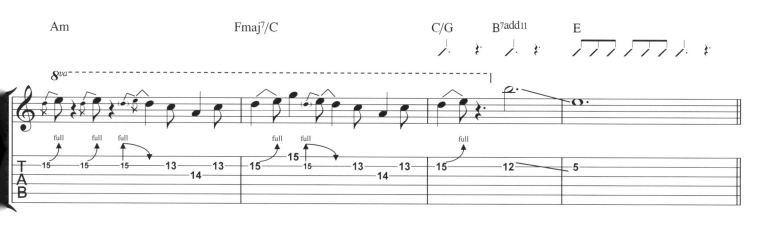

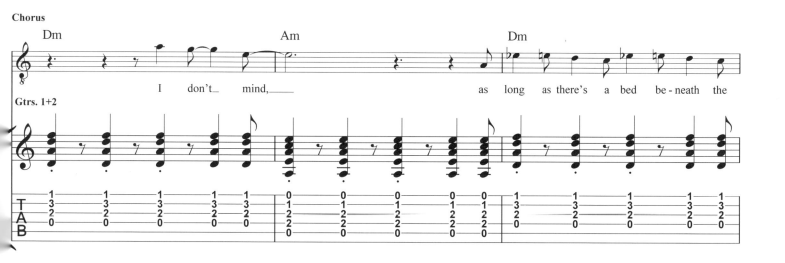

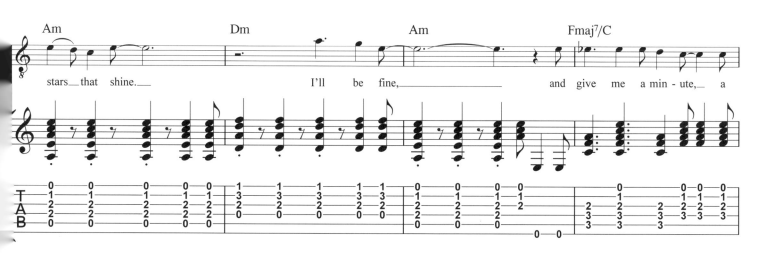

33

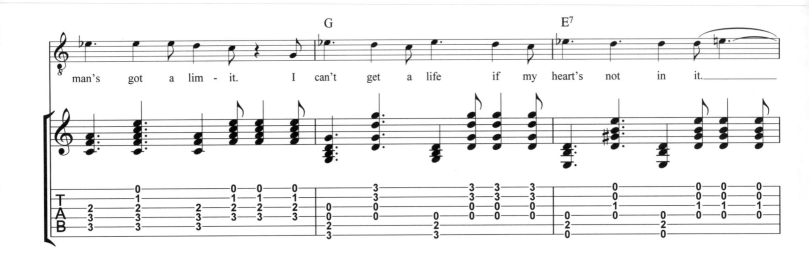

man's got a lim - it. I can't get a life if my heart's not in it.

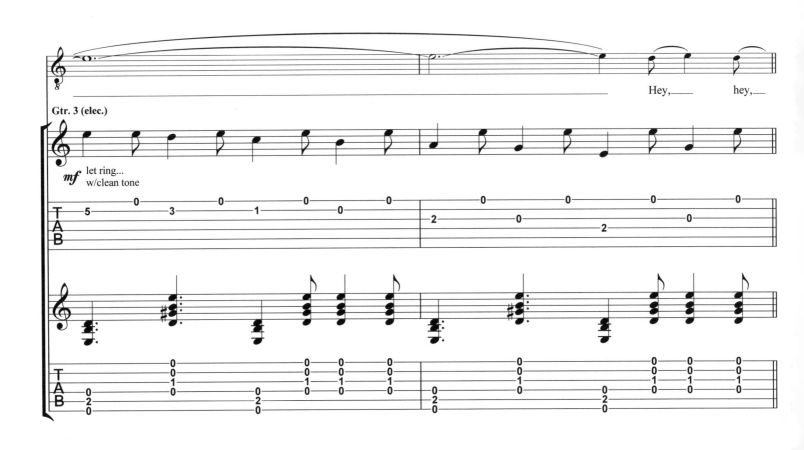

Hey,____ hey,____

Gtr. 3 (elec.)

mf let ring...
w/clean tone

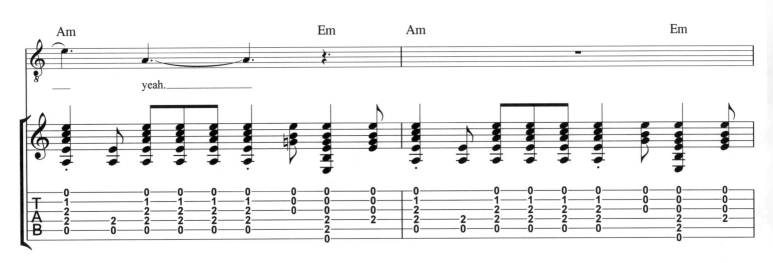

____ yeah._____

The Best Of You

Words & Music by
Dave Grohl, Taylor Hawkins, Nate Mendel & Chris Shiflett

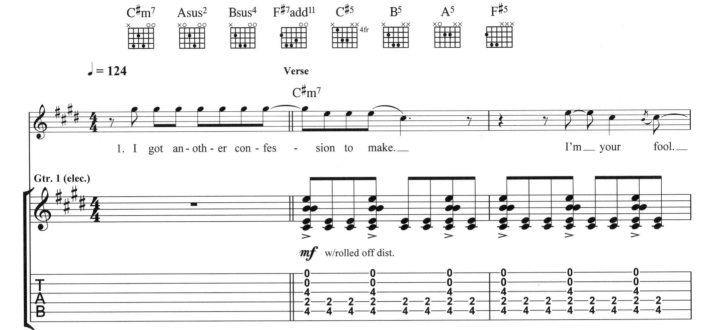

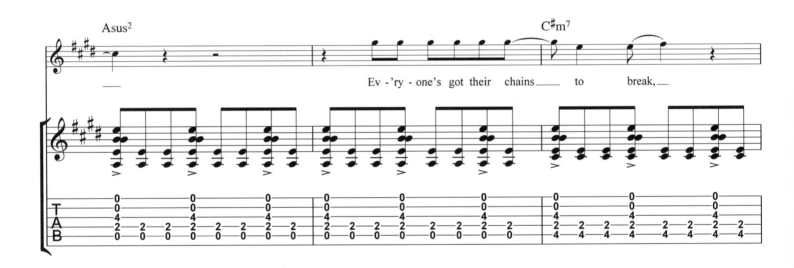

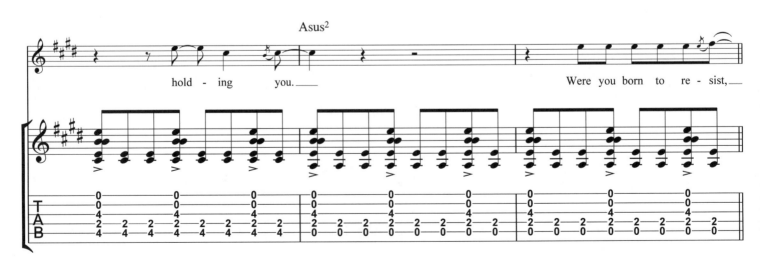

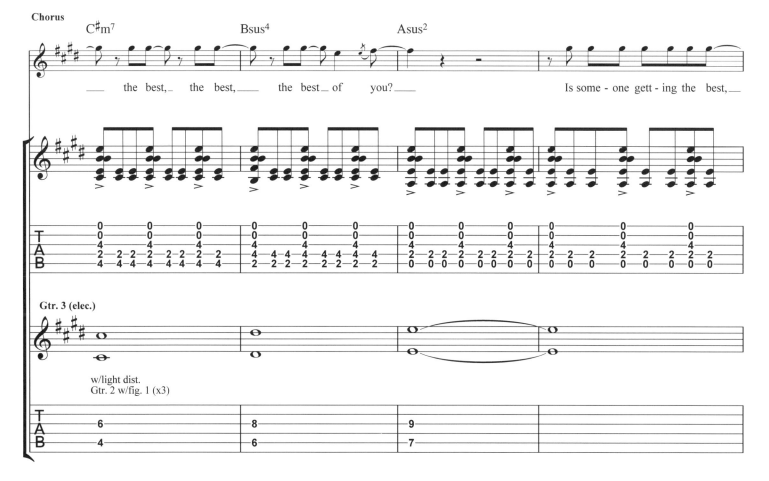

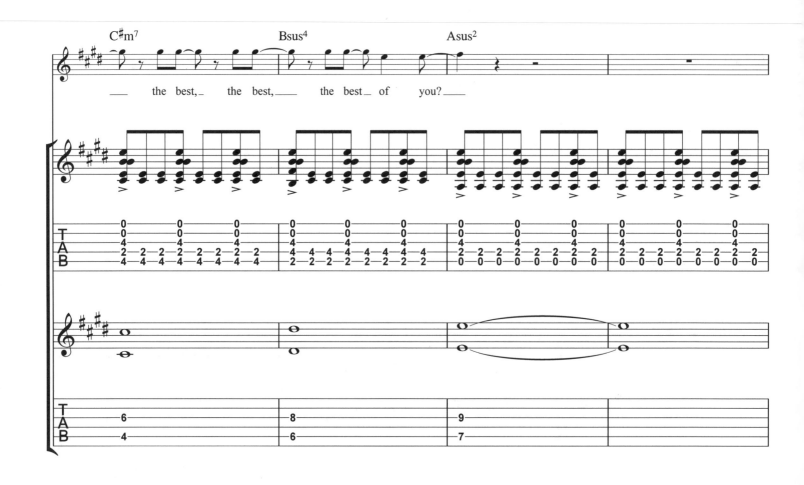

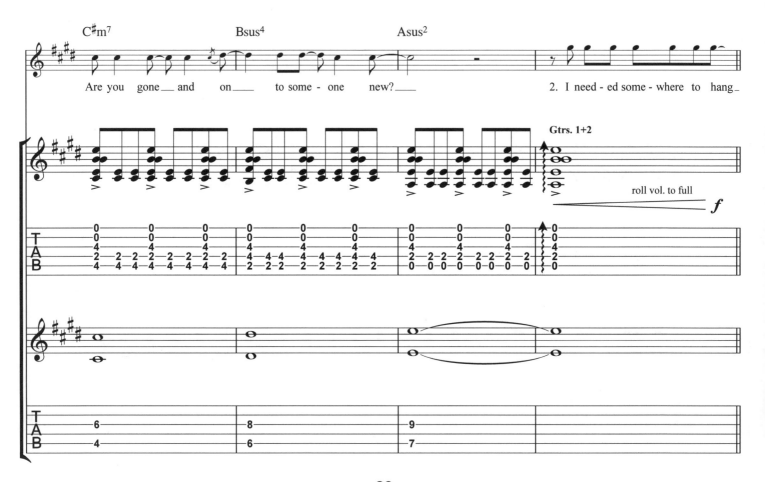

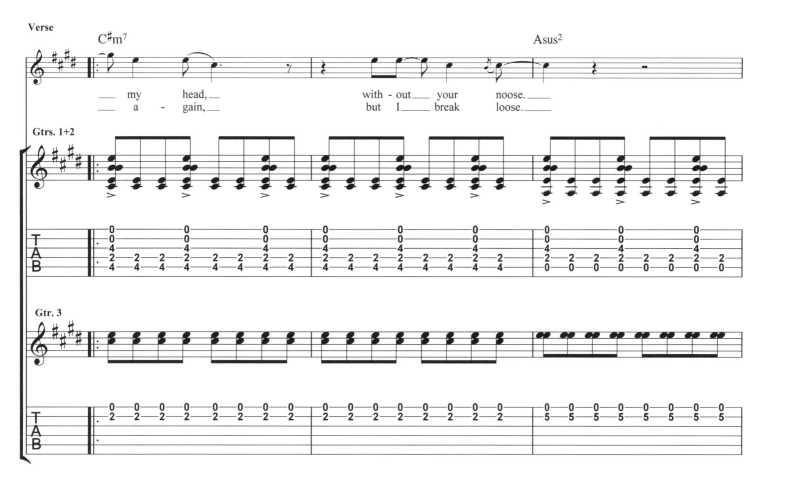

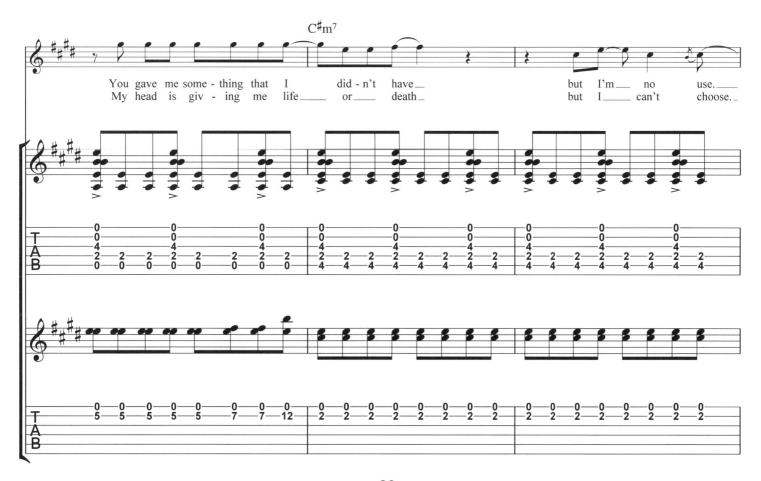

39

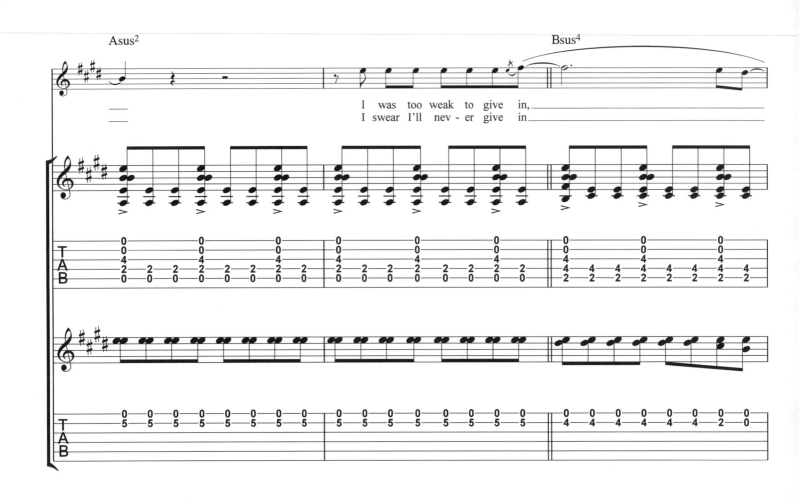

I was too weak to give in,
I swear I'll nev - er give in

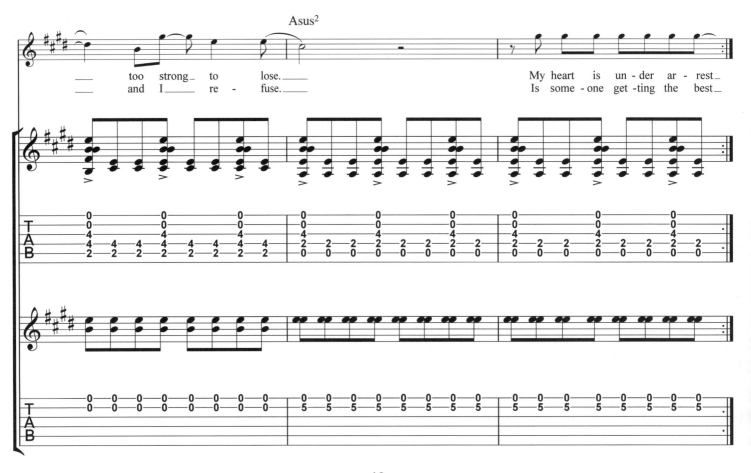

too strong to lose.
and I re - fuse.

My heart is un - der ar - rest
Is some - one get - ting the best

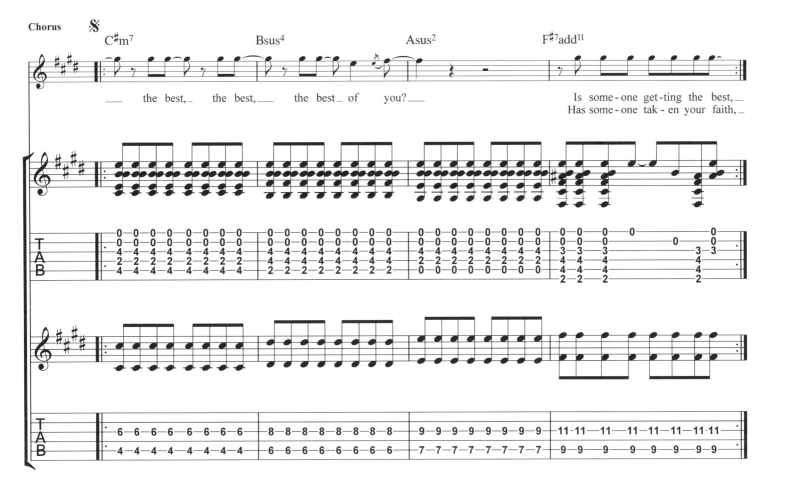

the best,___ the best,___ the best___ of you?___

Is some-one get-ting the best,___
Has some-one tak-en your faith,___

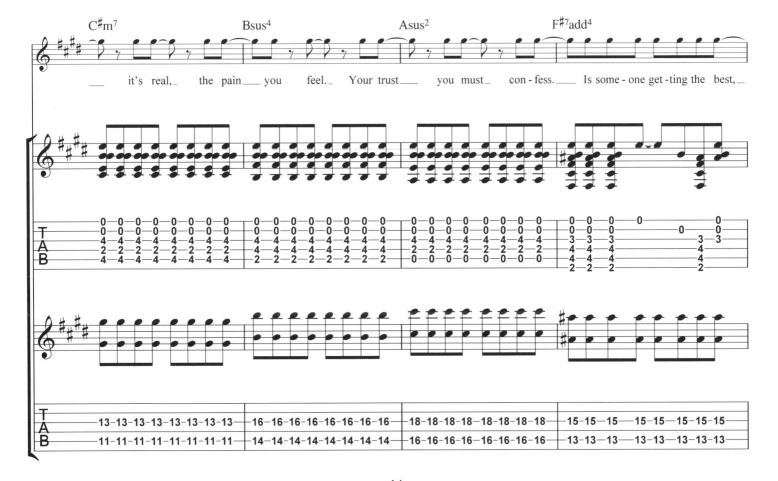

___ it's real,___ the pain___ you feel.___ Your trust___ you must___ con-fess.___ Is some-one get-ting the best,___

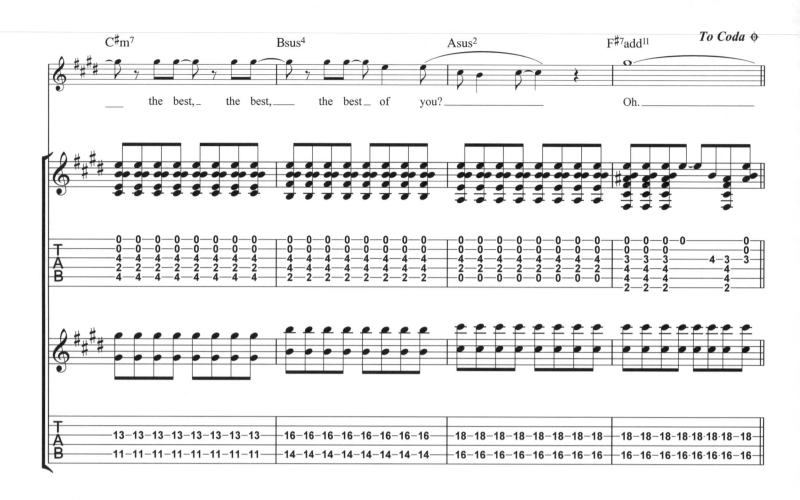

the best,＿ the best,＿ the best＿ of you?＿

Oh.＿

Interlude

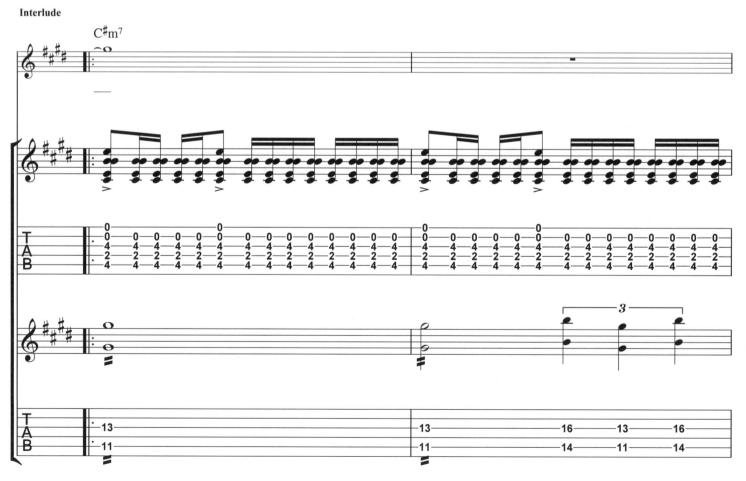

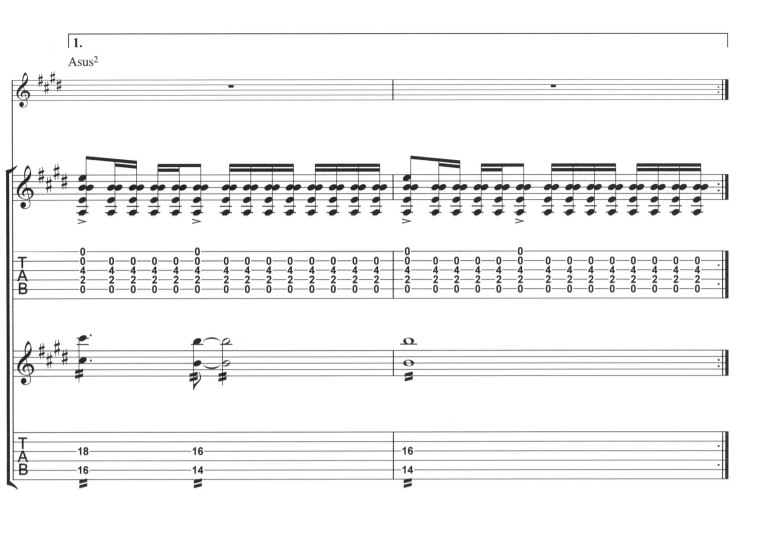

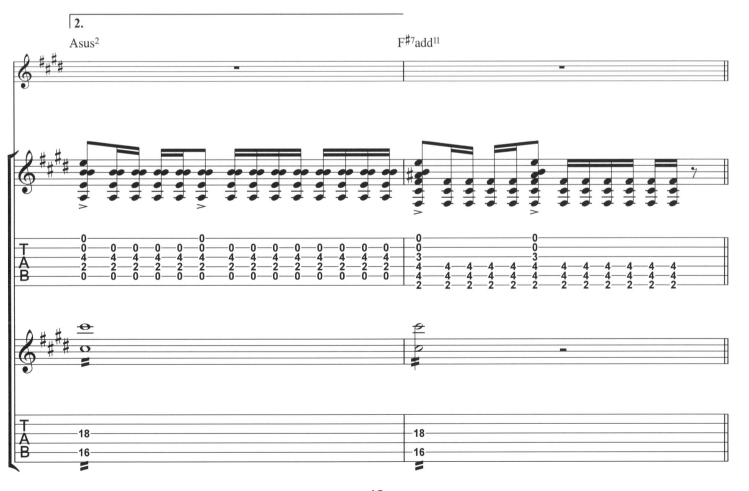

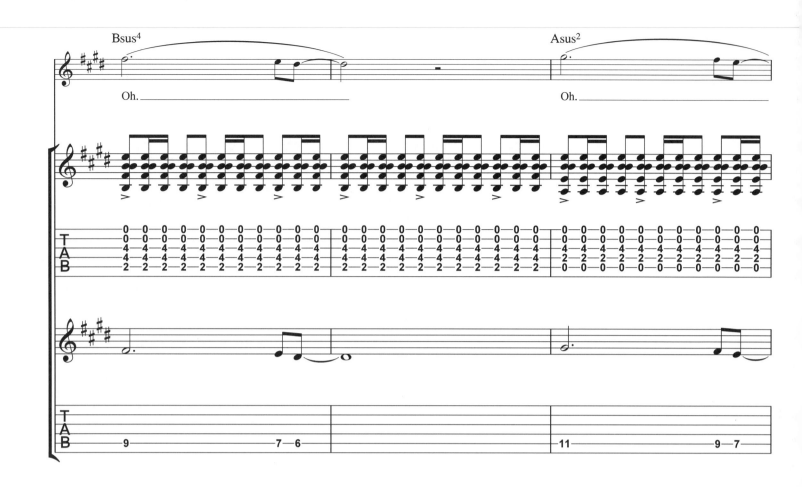

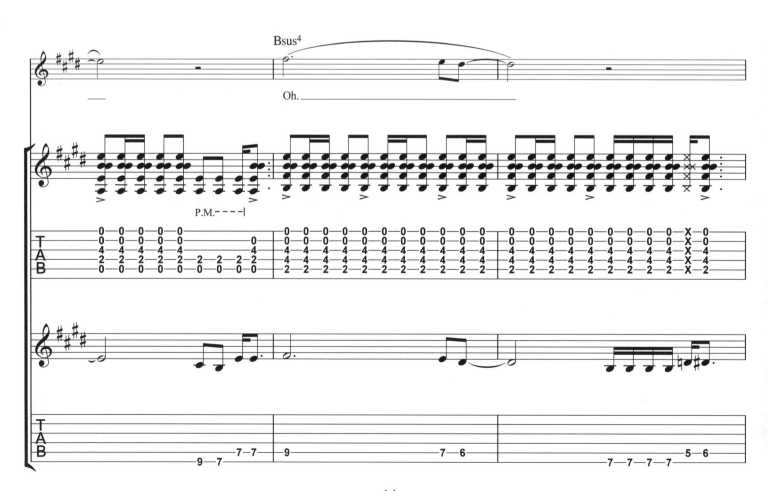

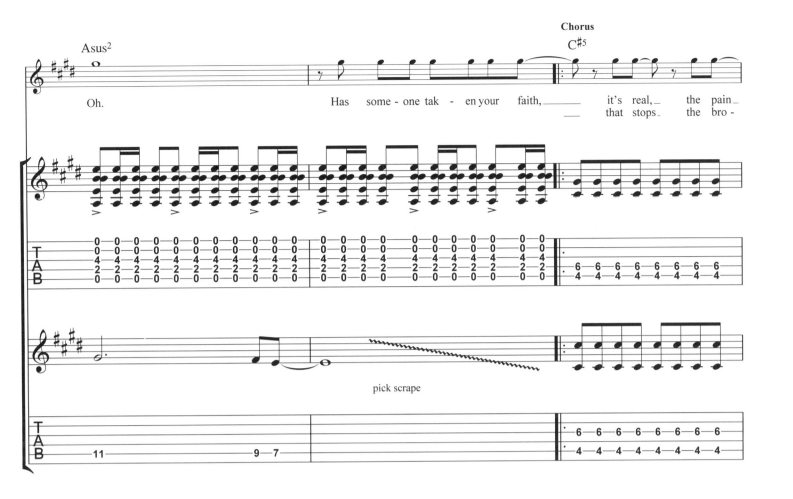

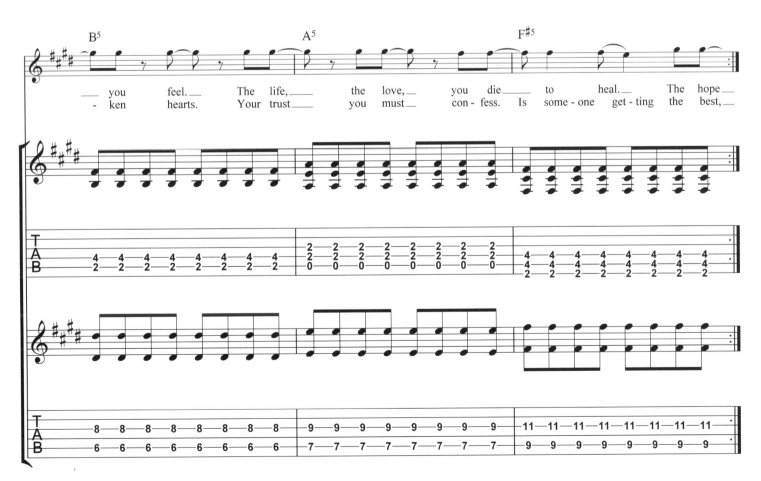

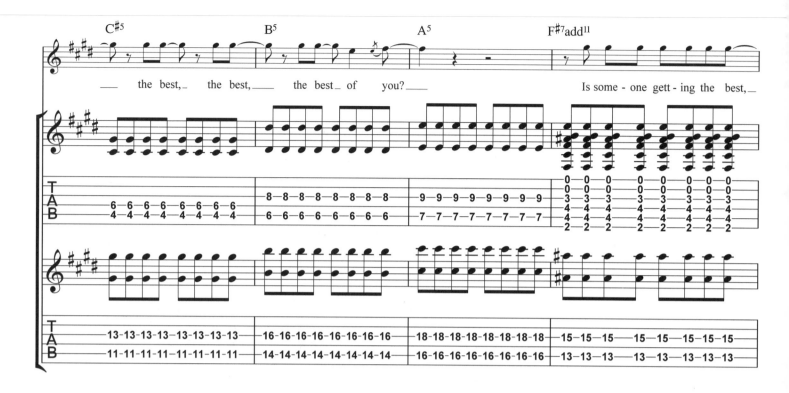

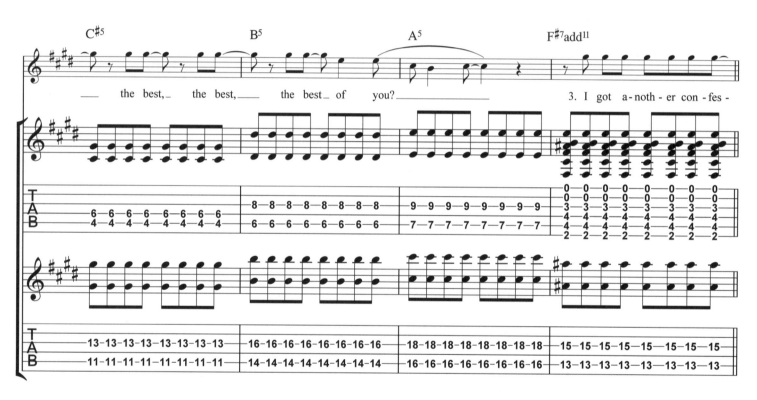

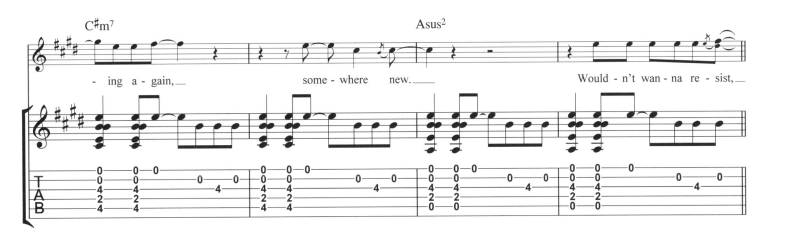

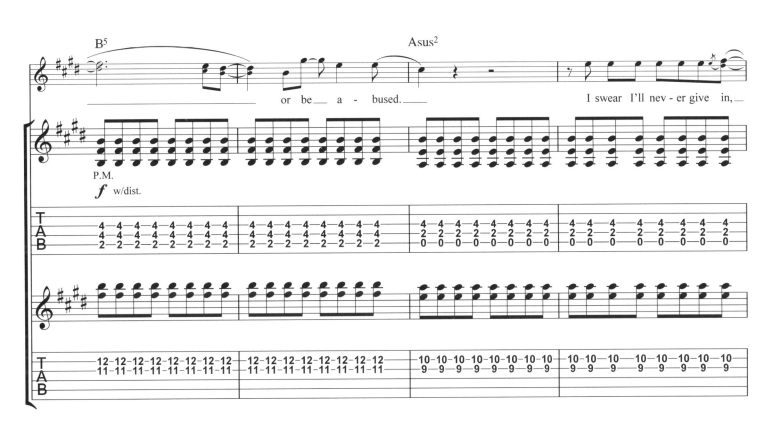

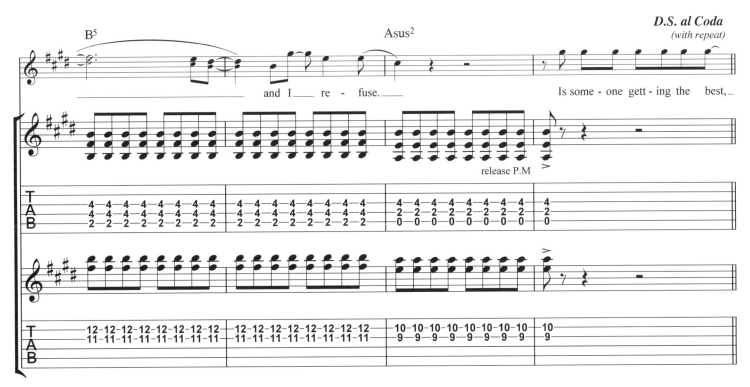

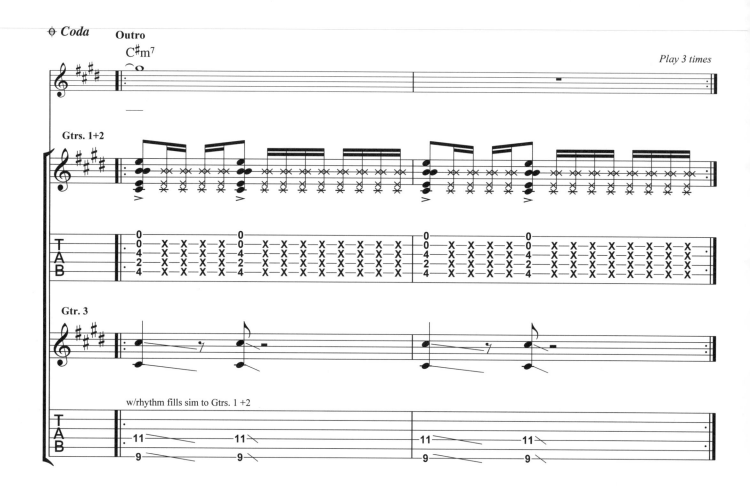

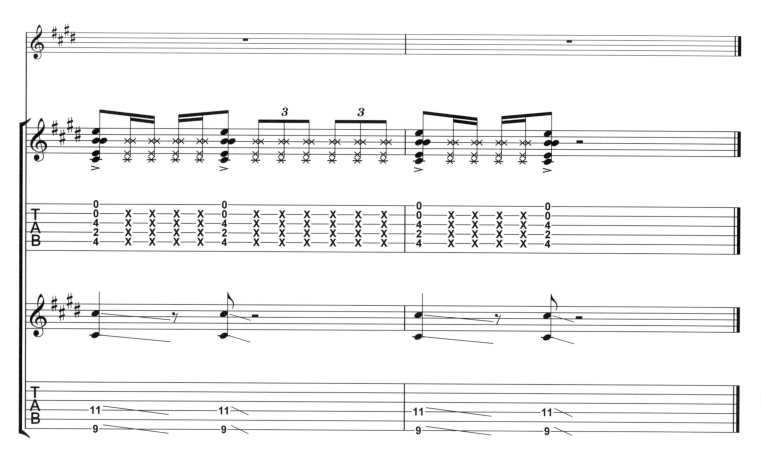

48

In My Head

Words & Music by
Josh Homme, Alain Johannes, Joey Castillo, Troy Van Leeuwen & Josh Freese

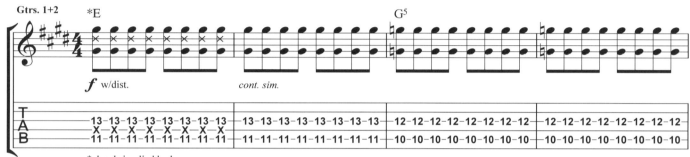

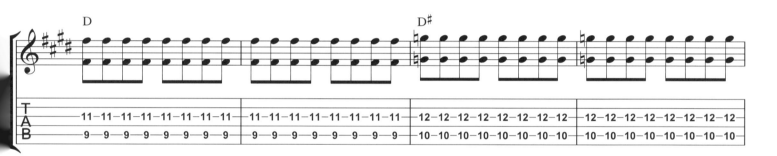

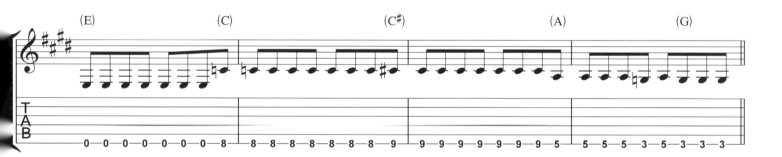

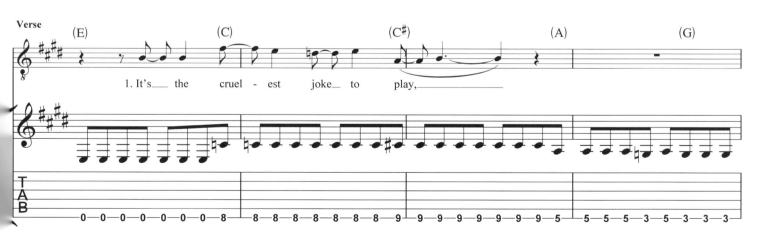

1. It's the cruel-est joke to play,

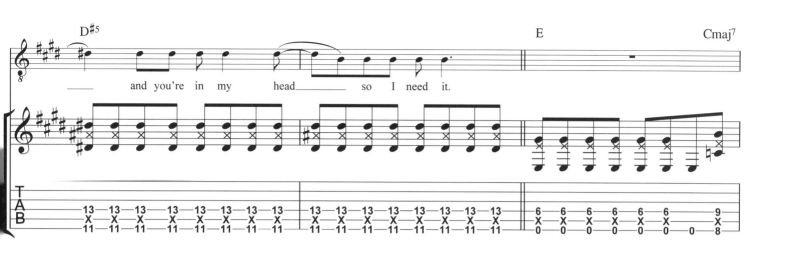

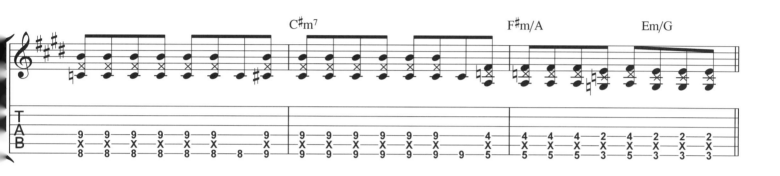

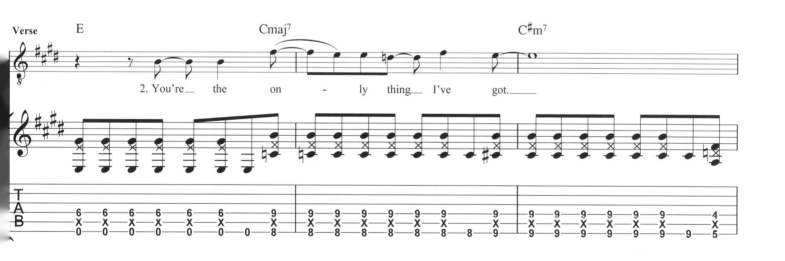

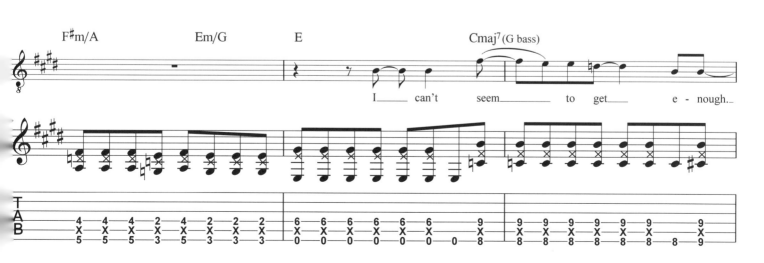

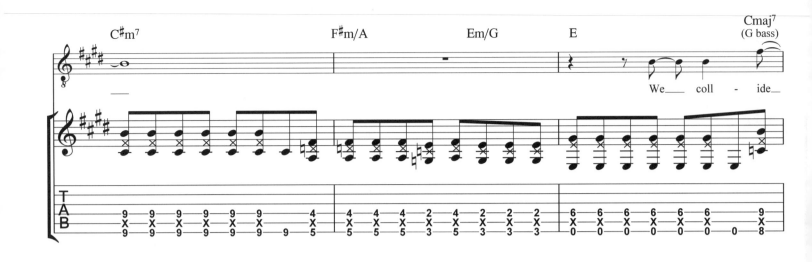

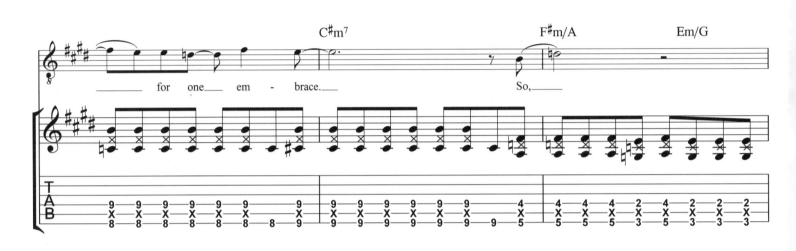

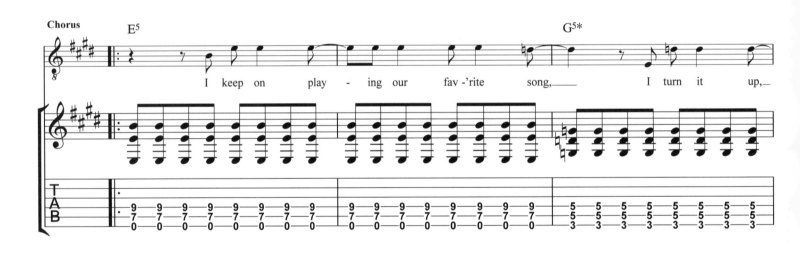

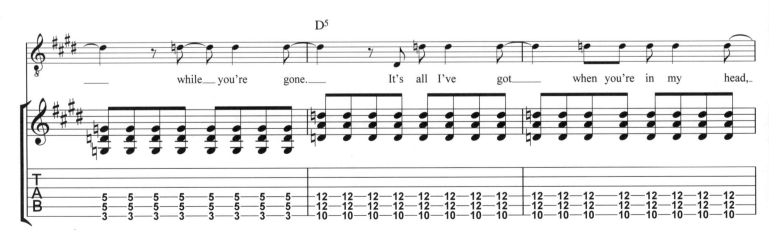

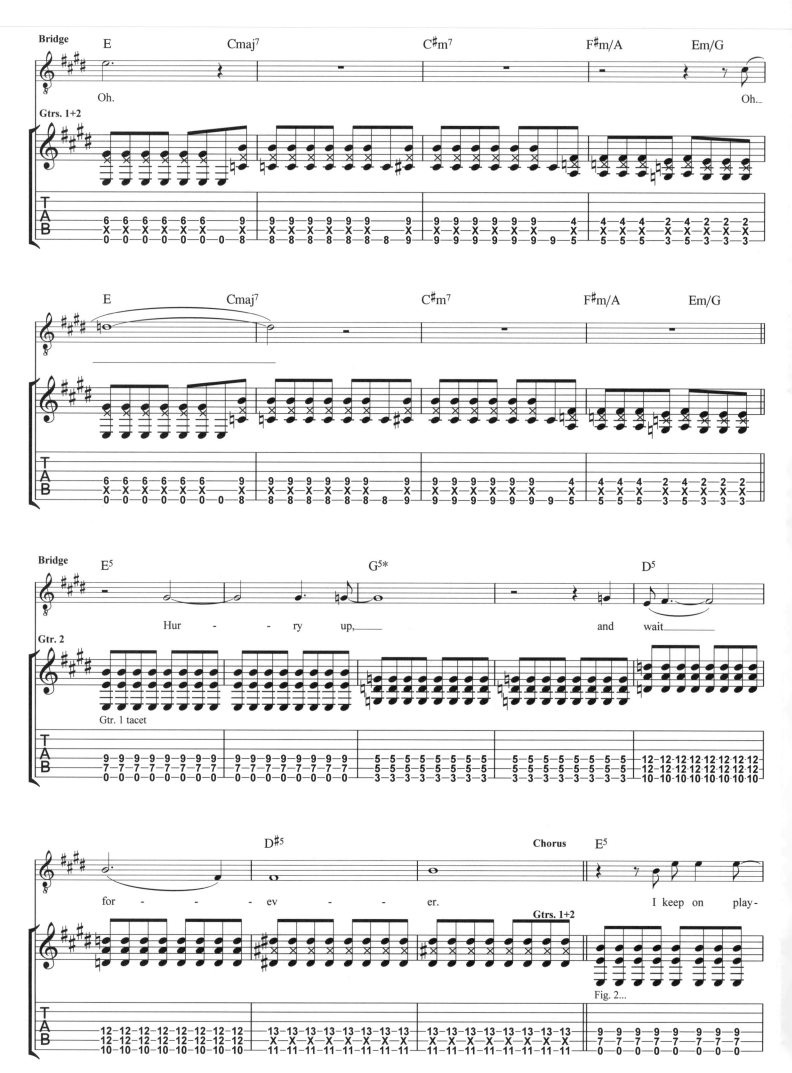

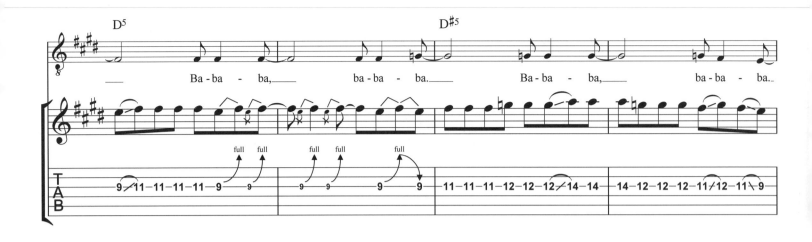

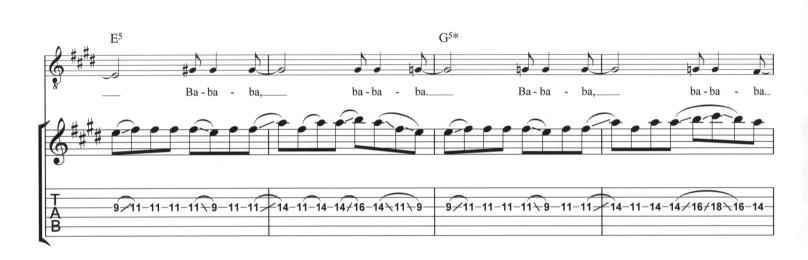

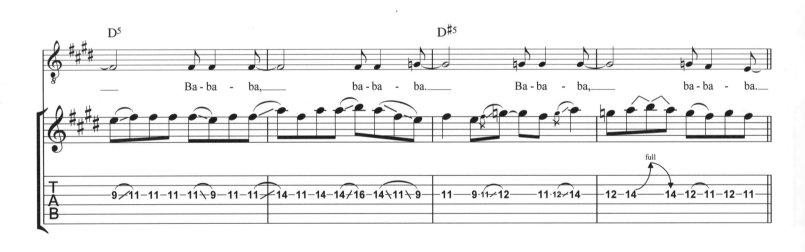

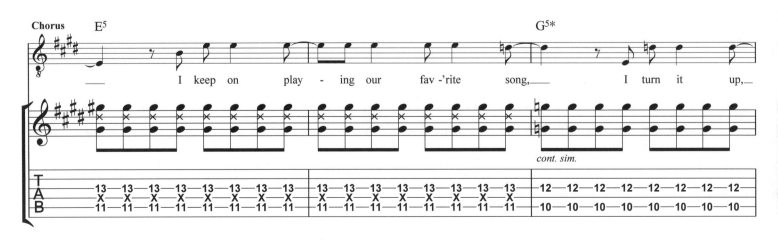

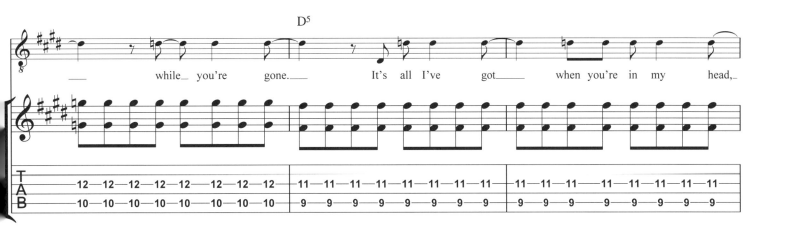

while you're gone.____ It's all I've got____ when you're in my head,____

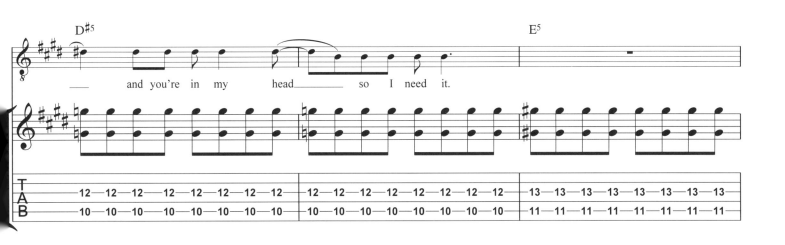

____ and you're in my head_____ so I need it.

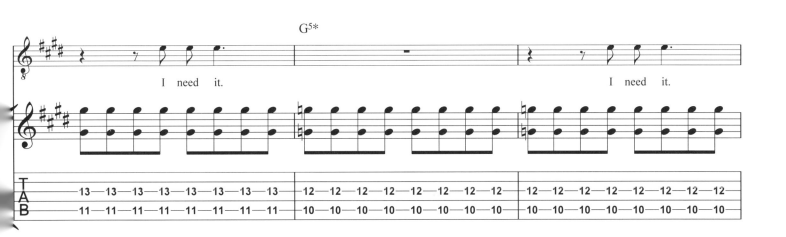

I need it. I need it.

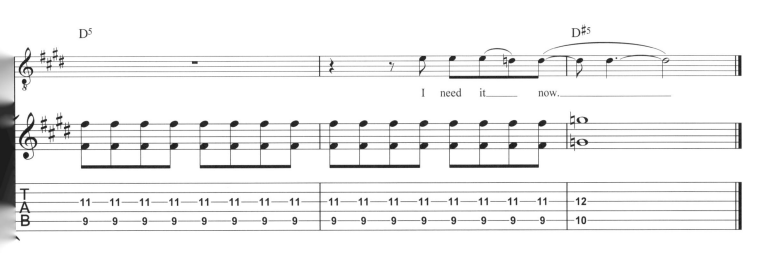

I need it_____ now._____

57

B.Y.O.B.

Words & Music by
Serj Tankian & Daron Malakian

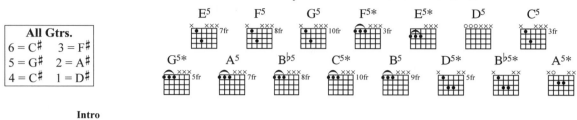

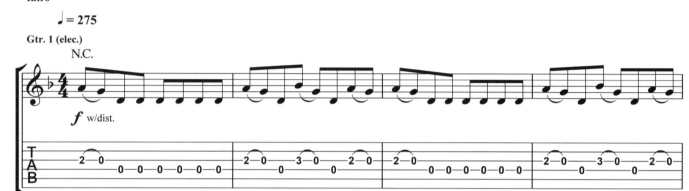

Intro

♩ = 275

Gtr. 1 (elec.)

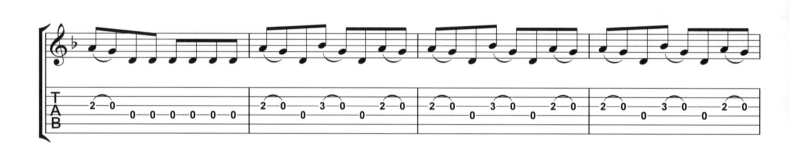

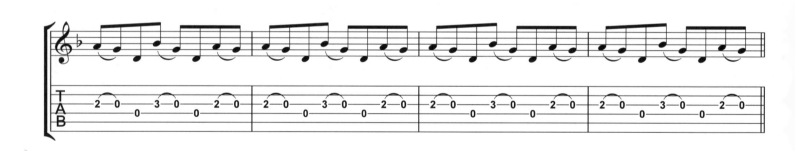

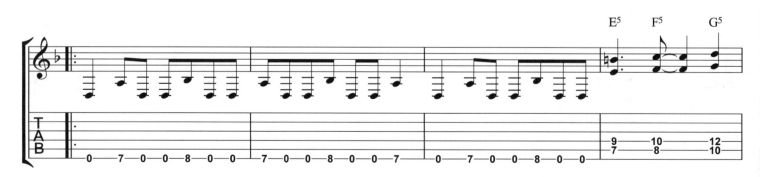

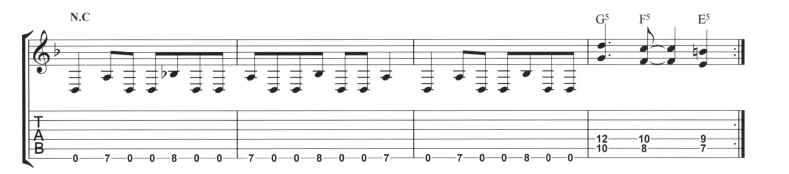

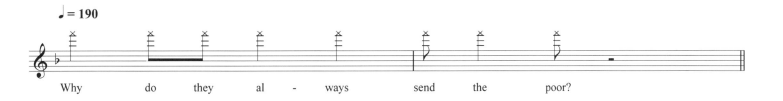

Why do they al - ways send the poor?

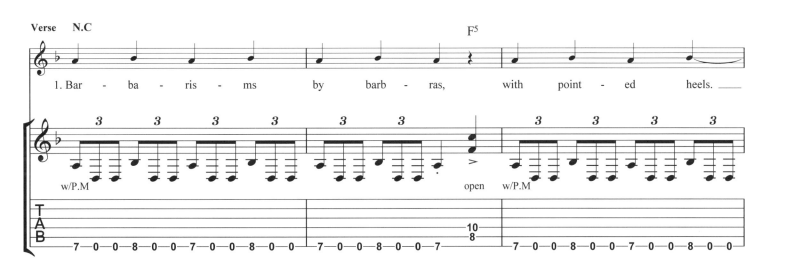

1. Bar - ba - ris - ms by barb - ras, with point - ed heels. ___

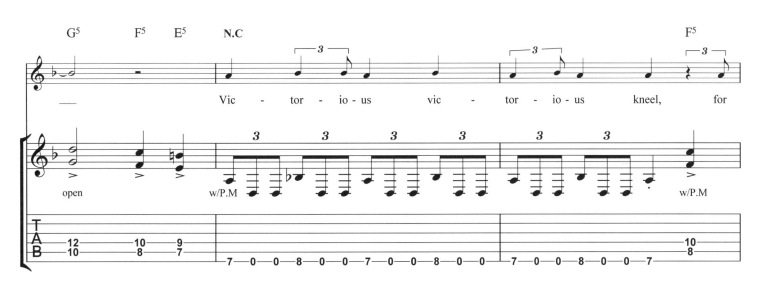

___ Vic - tor - io - us vic - tor - io - us kneel, for

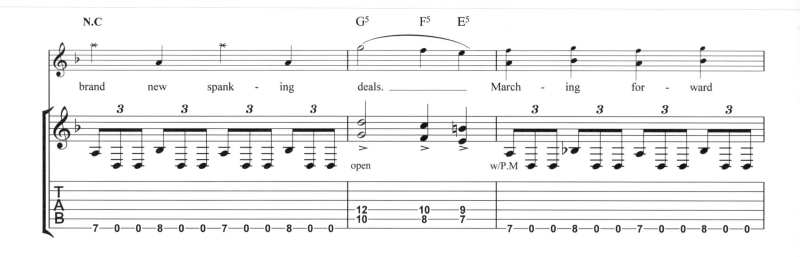

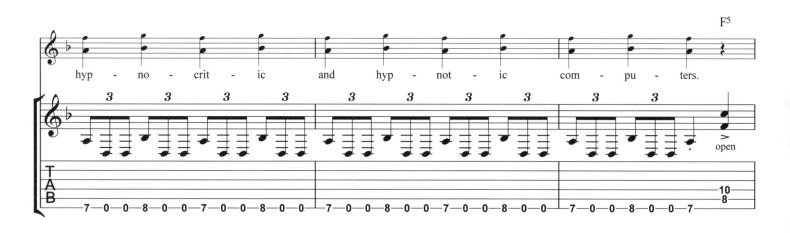

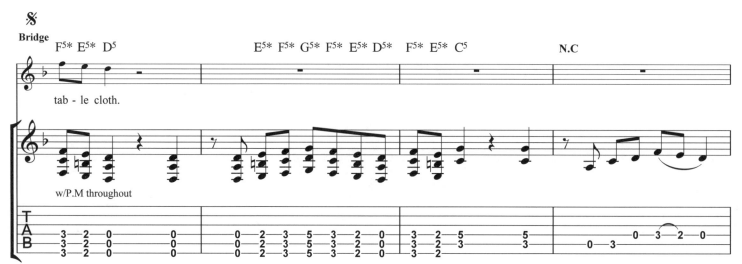

Original Feel

Verse N.C

2. Knee-ling ros-es dis-ap-pear-ing in-to Mos-es

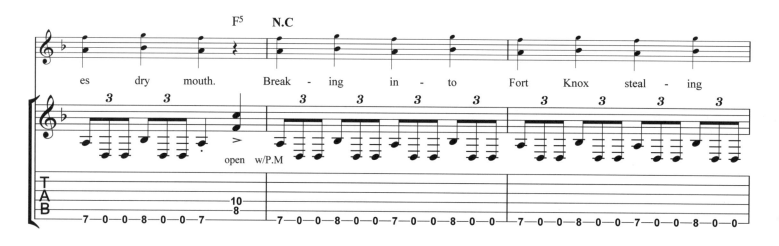

es dry mouth. Break-ing in-to Fort Knox steal-ing

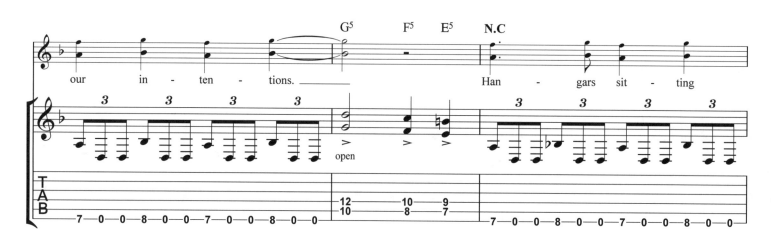

our in-ten-tions. Han-gars sit-ting

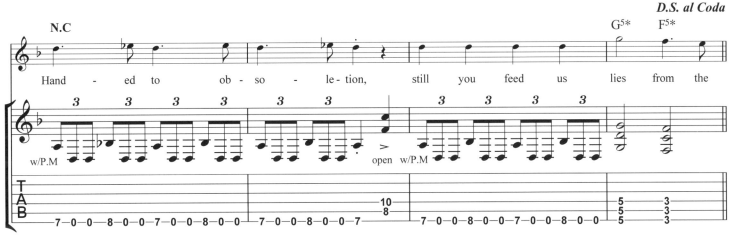

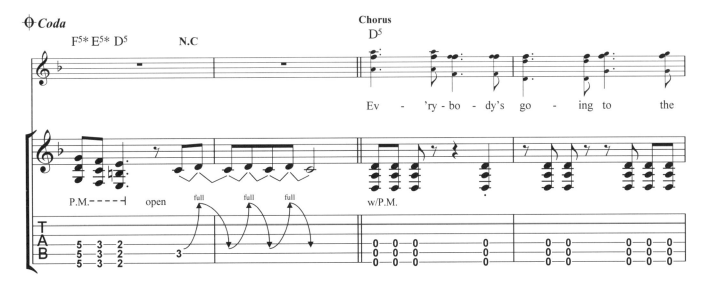

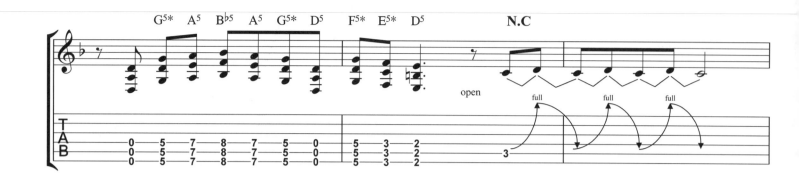

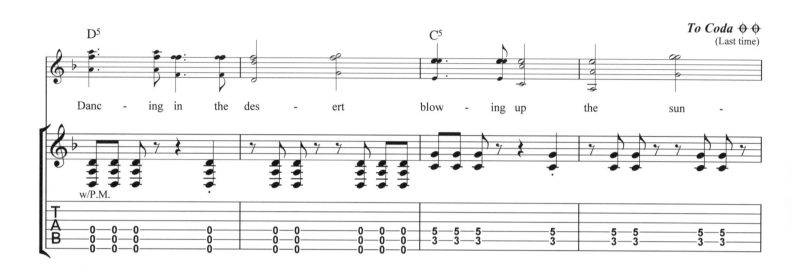

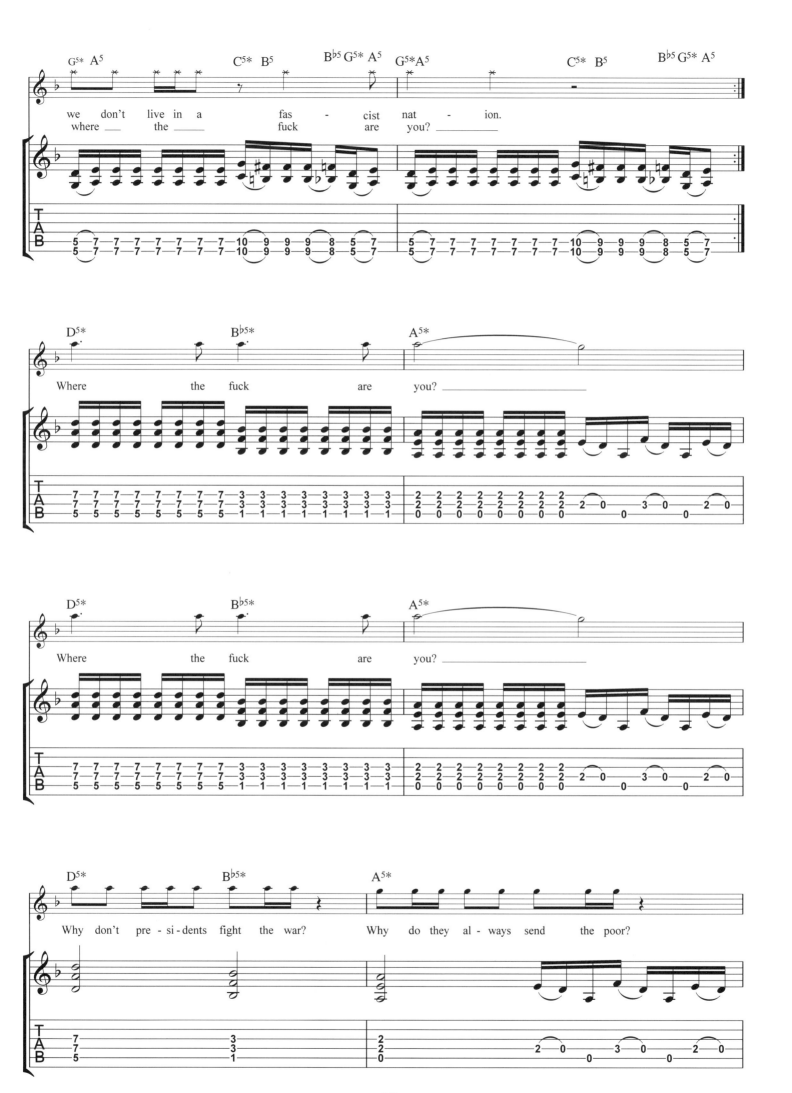

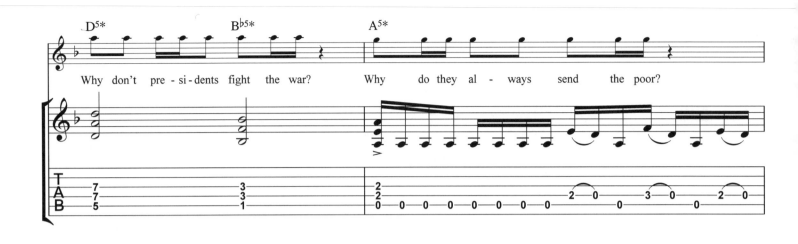

Why don't pre-si-dents fight the war? Why do they al-ways send the poor?

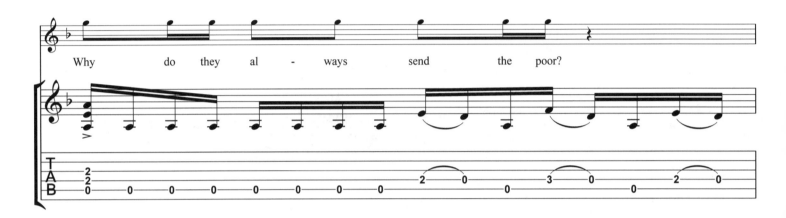

Why do they al-ways send the poor?

D.S.S al Coda
(Repeat D.S al Coda)

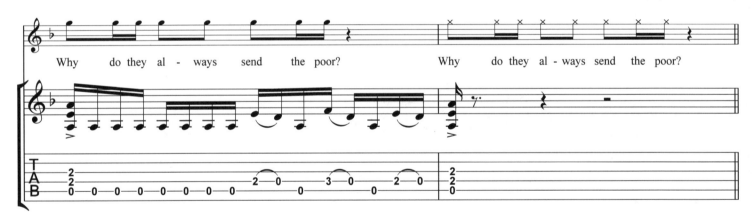

Why do they al-ways send the poor? Why do they al-ways send the poor?

Coda

(Double time feel)

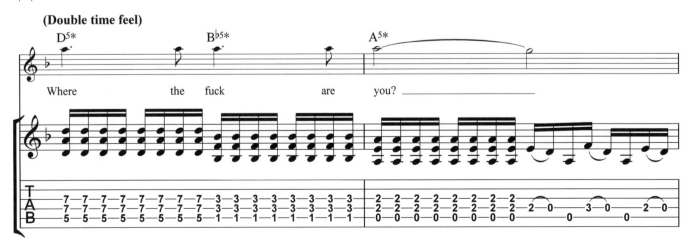

Where the fuck are you? _____

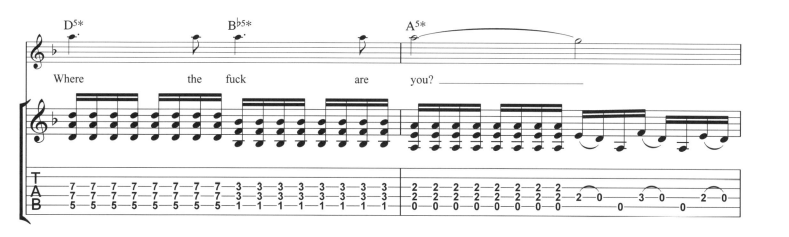

Where the fuck are you? _____

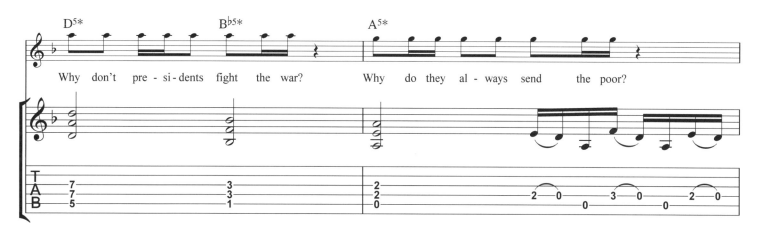

Why don't pre - si - dents fight the war? Why do they al - ways send the poor?

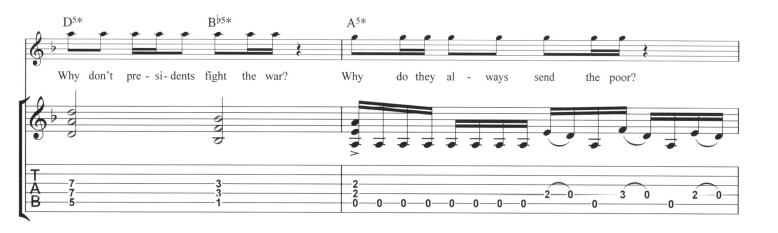

Why don't pre - si - dents fight the war? Why do they al - ways send the poor?

Why do they al - ways send the poor? Why do they al - ways send the poor?

pick evenly whilst sliding
down string towards nut.

Regular feel

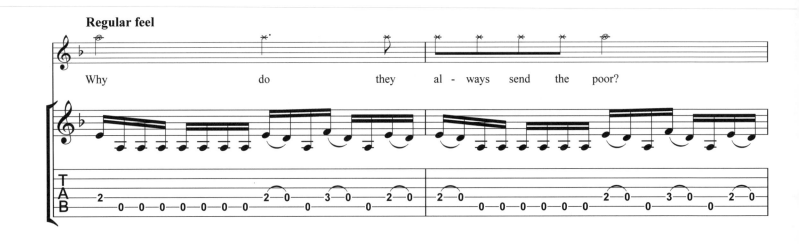

Why   do they al - ways send the poor?

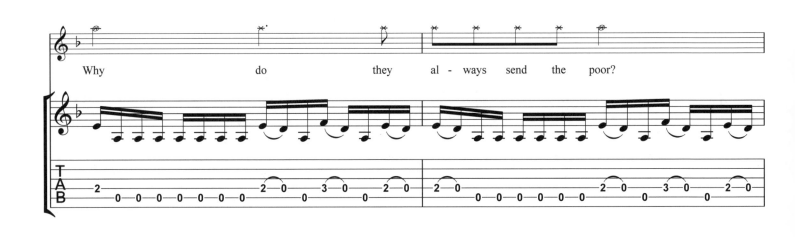

Why   do they al - ways send the poor?

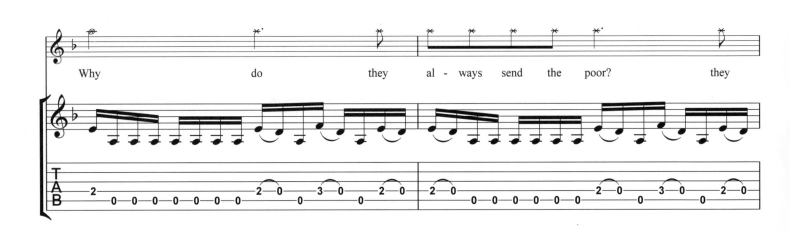

Why   do they al - ways send the poor?   they

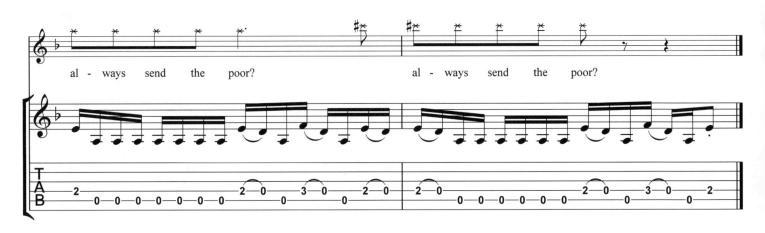

al - ways send the poor?   al - ways send the poor?

All Because Of You

Words by Bono
Music by U2

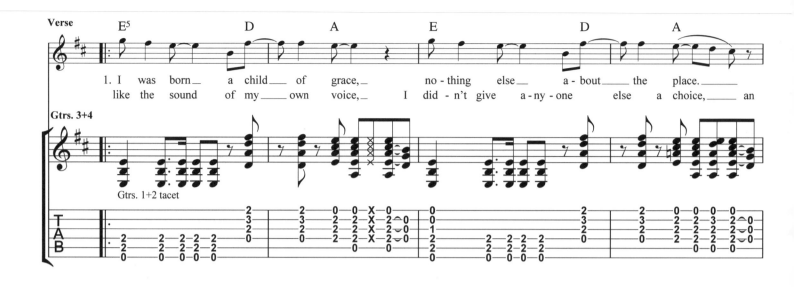

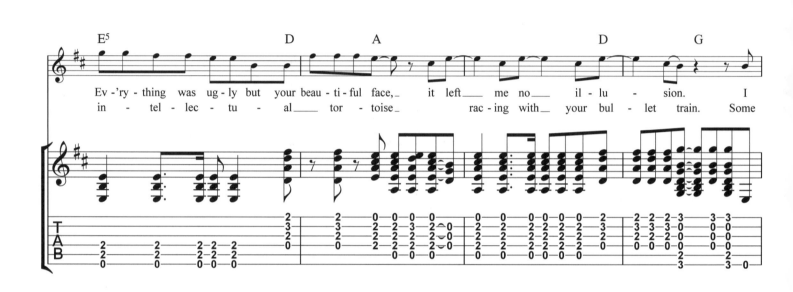

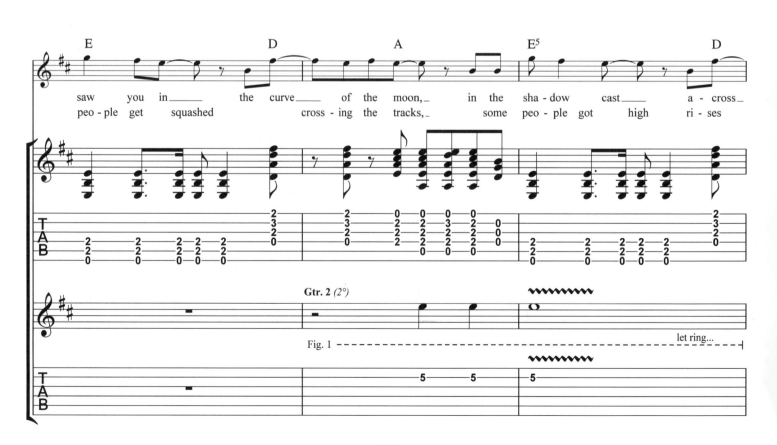

70

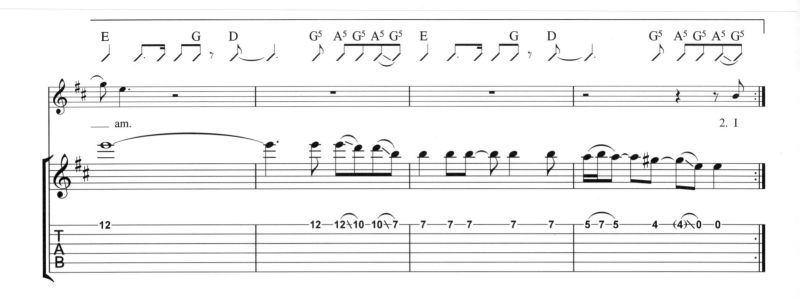

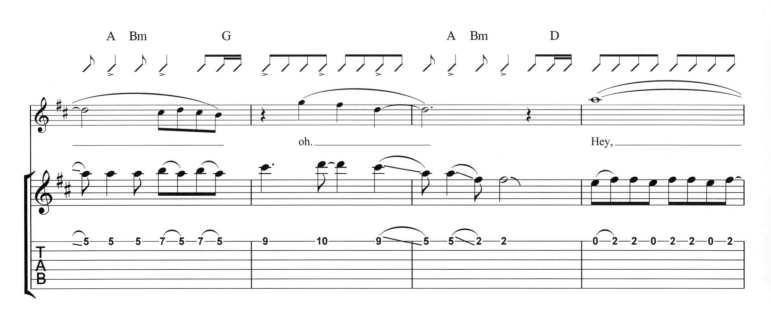

Going Missing

Words & Music by
Paul Smith, Thomas English, Duncan Lloyd, Archis Tiku & Lukas Wooller

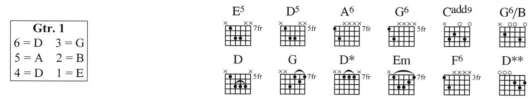

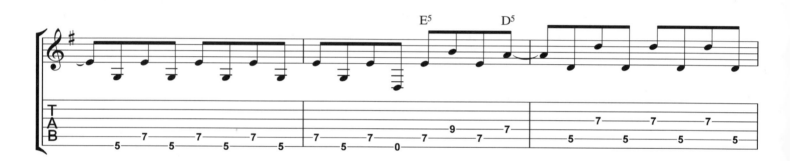

1. I sleep with my hands a-cross my chest, __ and I dream of you with some-one else.

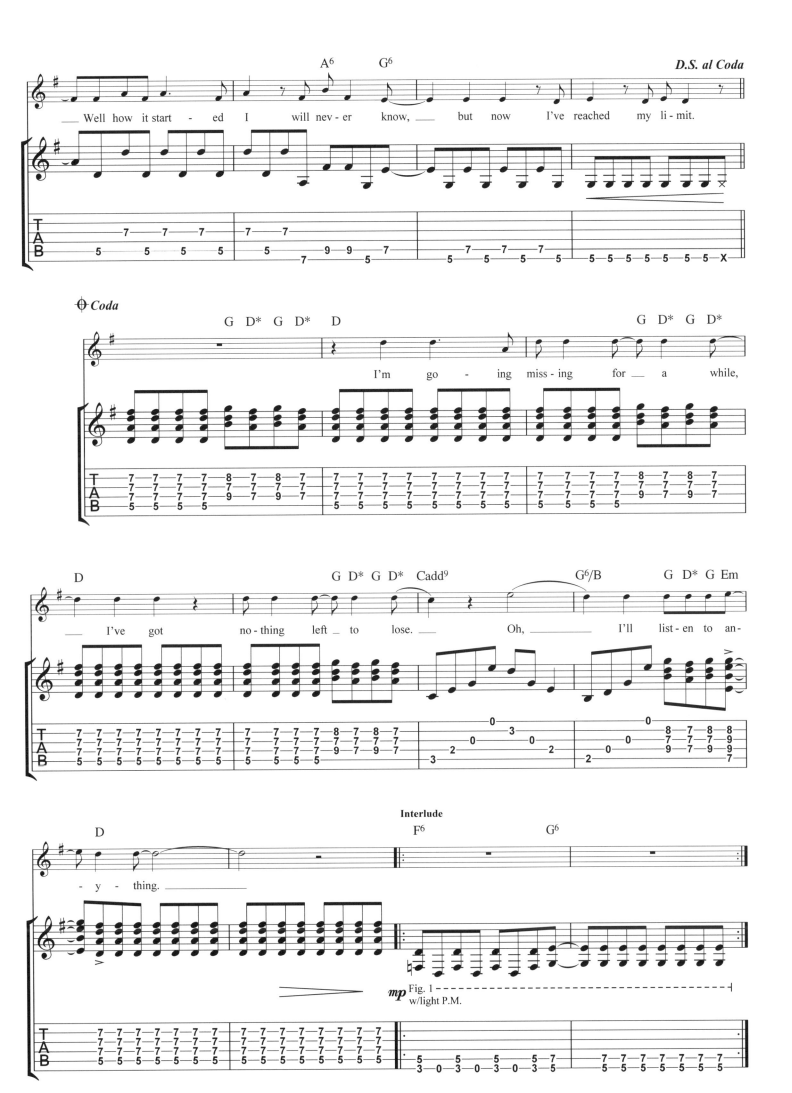

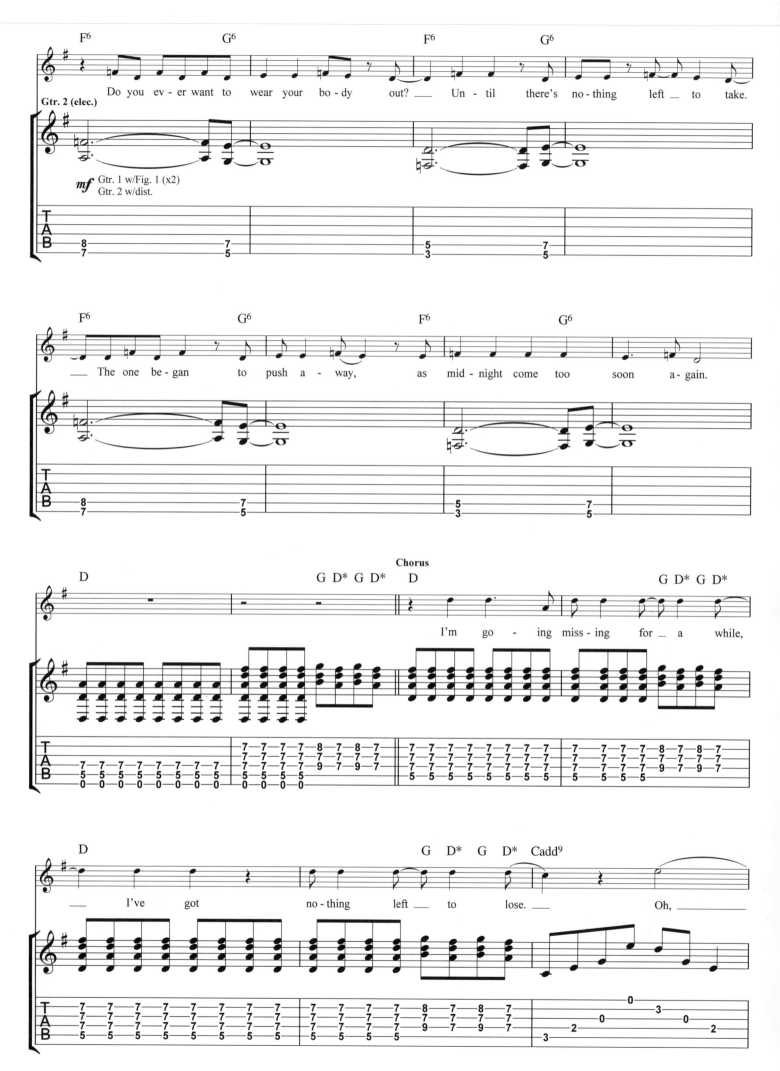

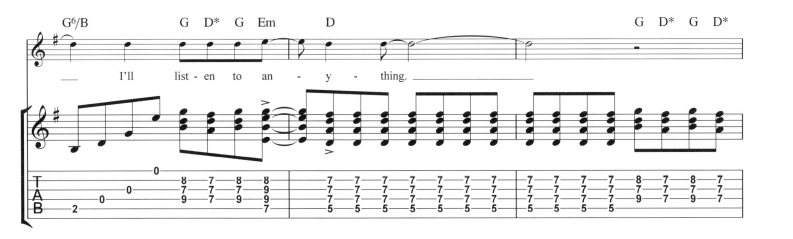

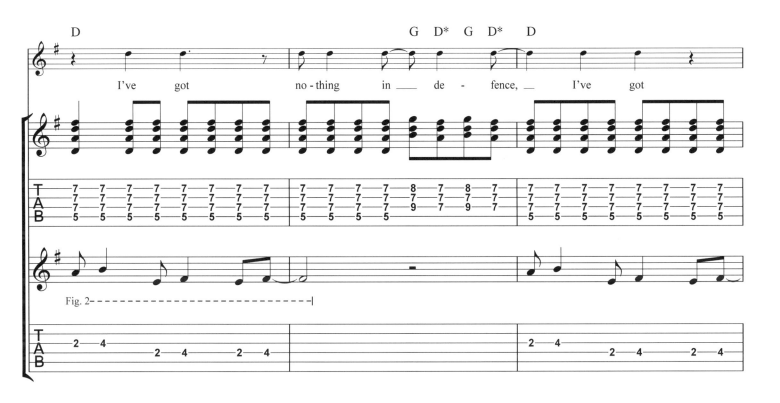

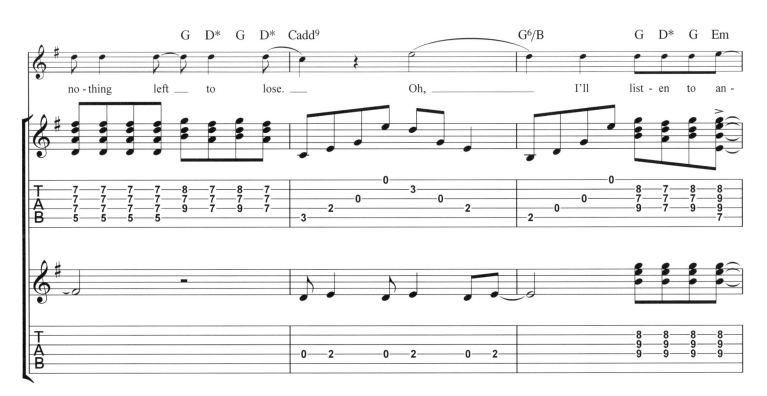

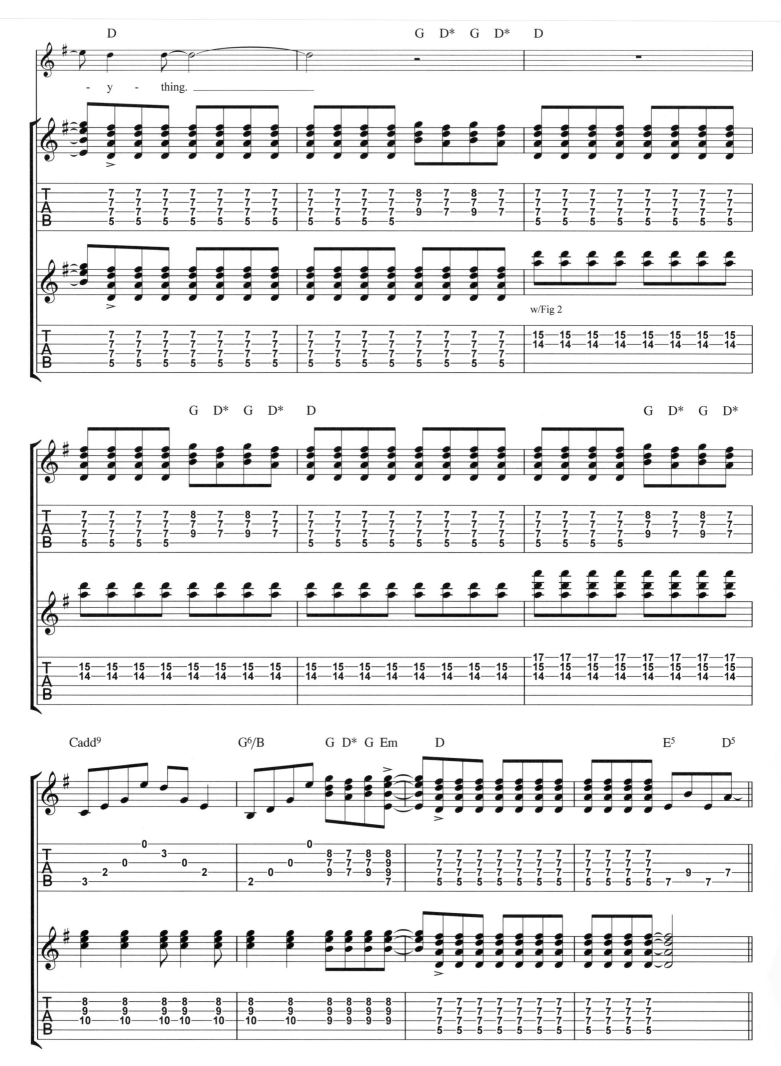

82

Outro

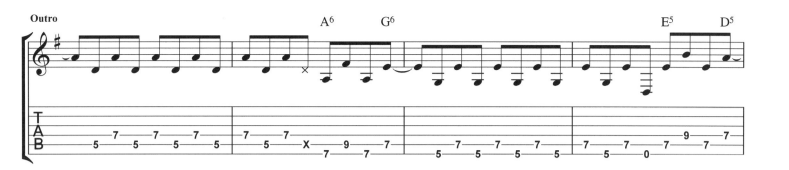

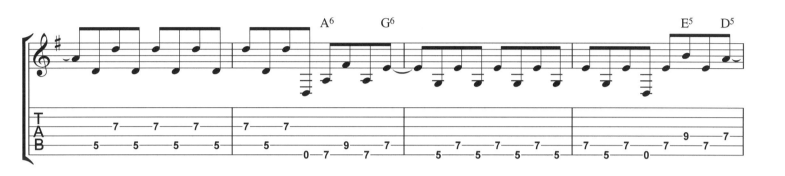

I sleep with my hands a - cross ____ my

chest, and I dream of you with some - one else. _____

Somewhere Else

Words & Music by
Johnny Borrell

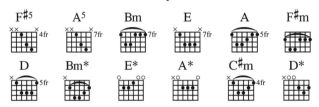

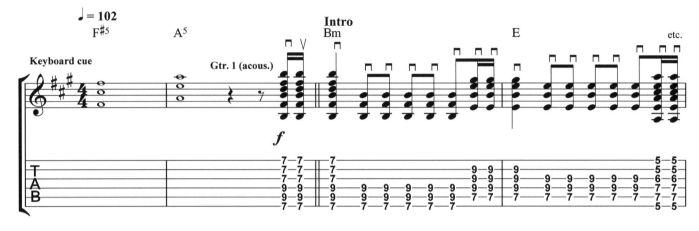

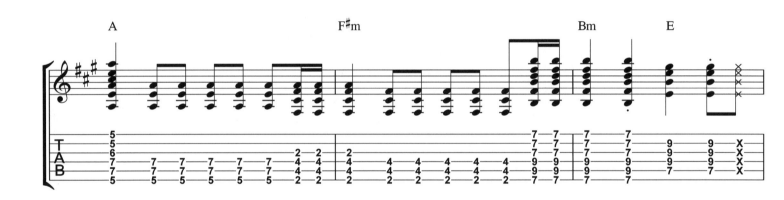

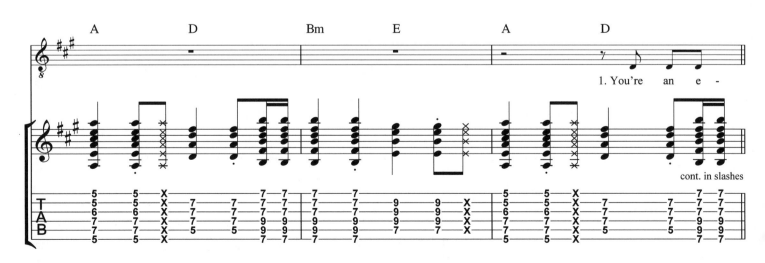

1. You're an e -

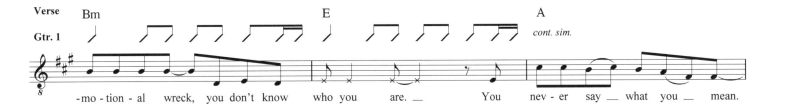

-mo - tion - al wreck, you don't know who you are. ___ You nev - er say ___ what you ___ mean.

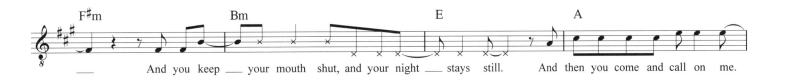

___ And you keep ___ your mouth shut, and your night ___ stays still. And then you come and call on me.

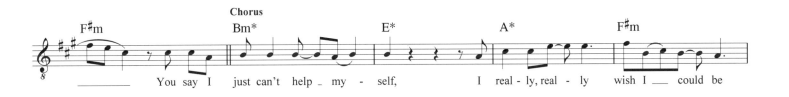

_____ You say I just can't help ___ my - self, I real - ly, real - ly wish I ___ could be

some - where else ___ than here. ___ 2. And I met a girl,
3. She looked at me, ___

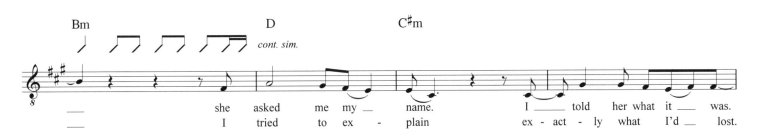

___ she asked me my ___ name. I ___ told her what it ___ was.
___ I tried to ex - plain ex - act - ly what I'd ___ lost.

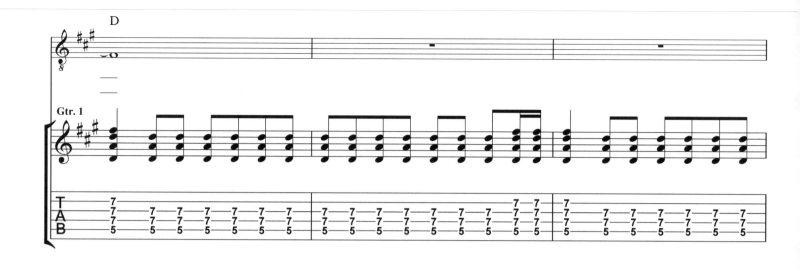

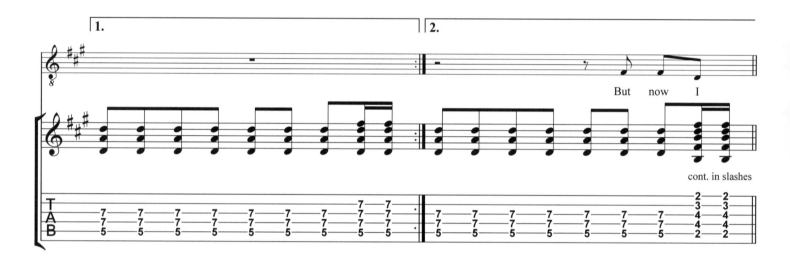

Chorus

just can't help _ my - self, I real - ly, real - ly wish I __ could be

some - where else ___ than here. ___ You give me

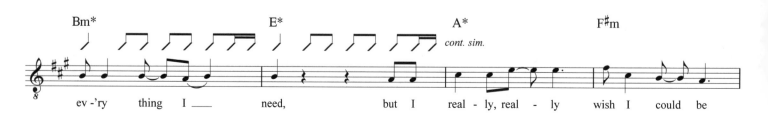

ev -'ry thing I ___ need, but I real - ly, real - ly wish I could be

some - where else _____ than here. _____ Just an-y-where else,

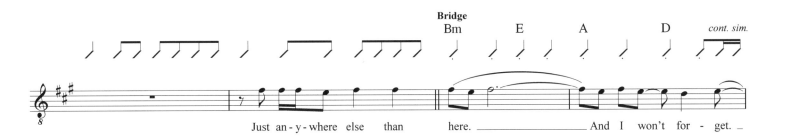

Bridge

Just an-y-where else than here. _____ And I won't for - get. _____

_____ No, I won't for - get. _____ No, I won't for - get.

Verse

_____ 4. Oh, when I saw you there, it was the _____ first time, _ and

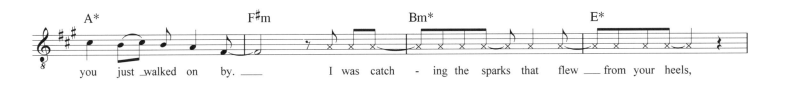

you just _walked on by. _____ I was catch - ing the sparks that flew _____ from your heels,

try - ing to catch your eye. _____ But that was some - where else, there's

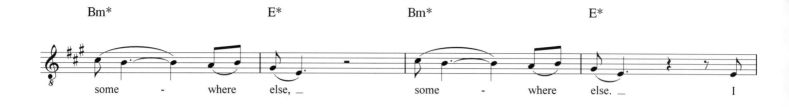

some - where else, ___ some - where else. ___ I

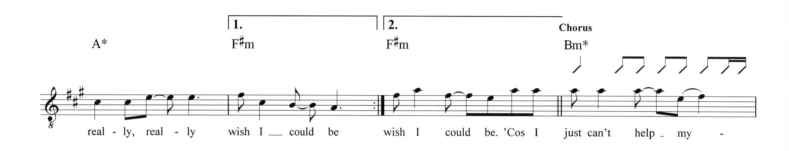

1. **2.** **Chorus**

real - ly, real - ly wish I ___ could be wish I could be. 'Cos I just can't help ___ my -

cont. sim.

- self, I real - ly, real - ly wish I ___ could be some - where else ___ than here.

___ And now I

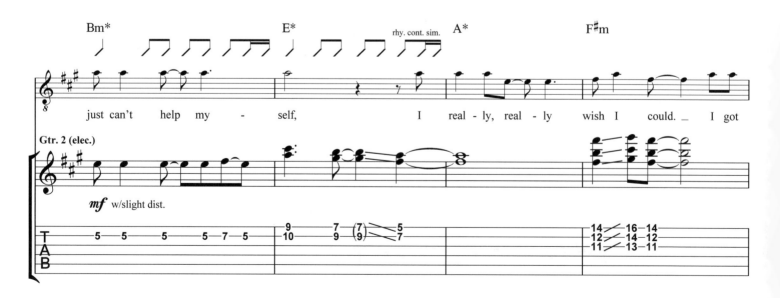

just can't help my - self, I real - ly, real - ly wish I could. ___ I got

Gtr. 2 (elec.)

mf w/slight dist.

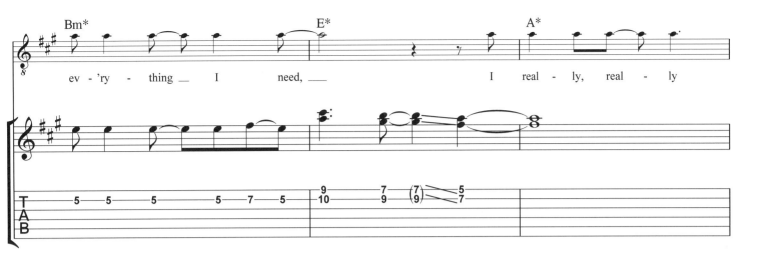

ev - 'ry - thing __ I need, __ I real - ly, real - ly

rall.

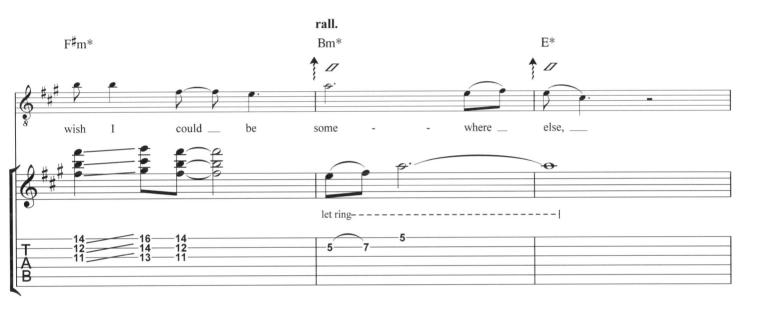

wish I could __ be some - - where __ else, __

let ring - |

Gtr. 2 tacet

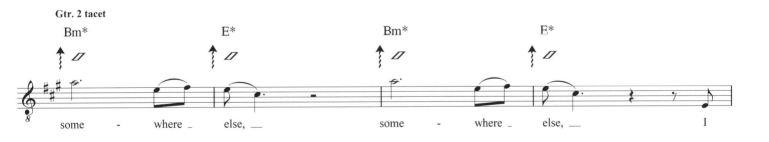

some - where _ else, __ some - where _ else, __ I

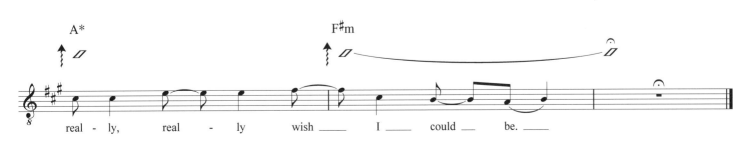

real - ly, real - ly wish __ I __ could __ be. __

89

Smile Like You Mean It

Words & Music by
Brandon Flowers, Dave Keuning, Mark Stoermer & Ronnie Vannucci

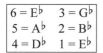

Intro

Keyboard arr. for Gtr.

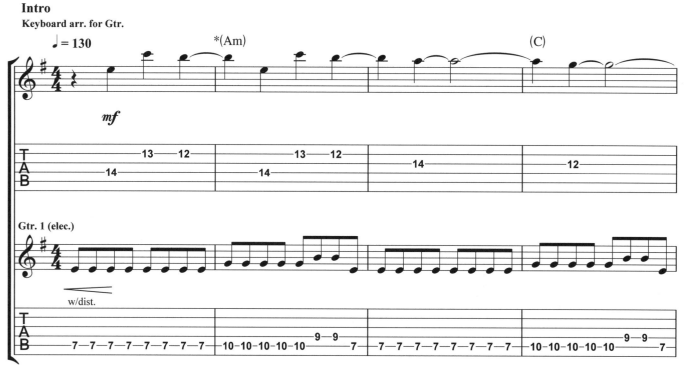

*chords implied by bass

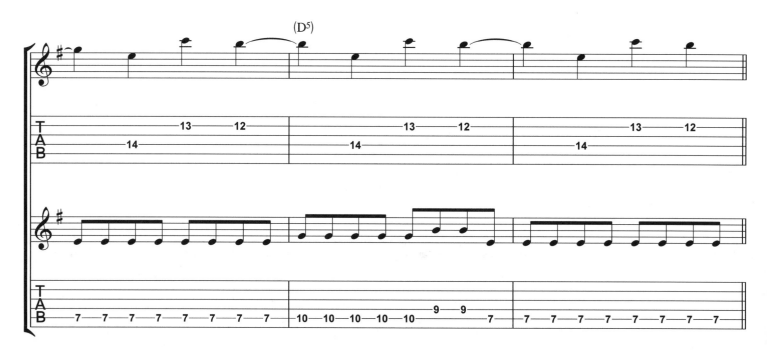

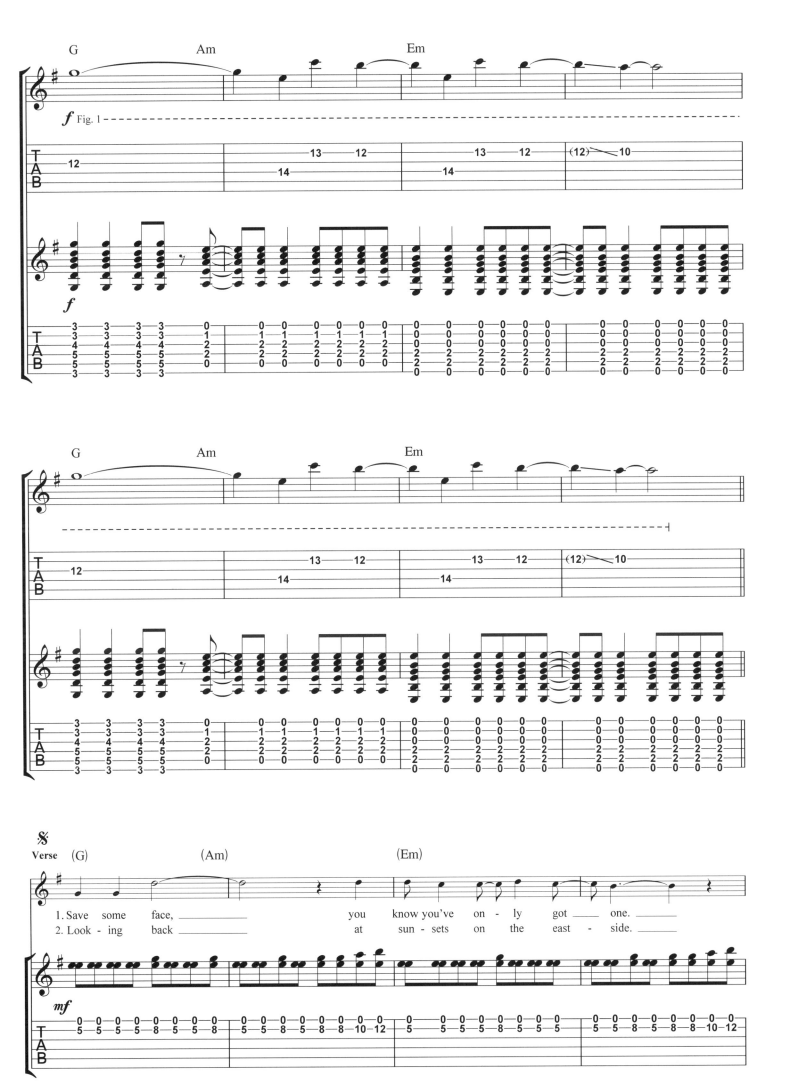

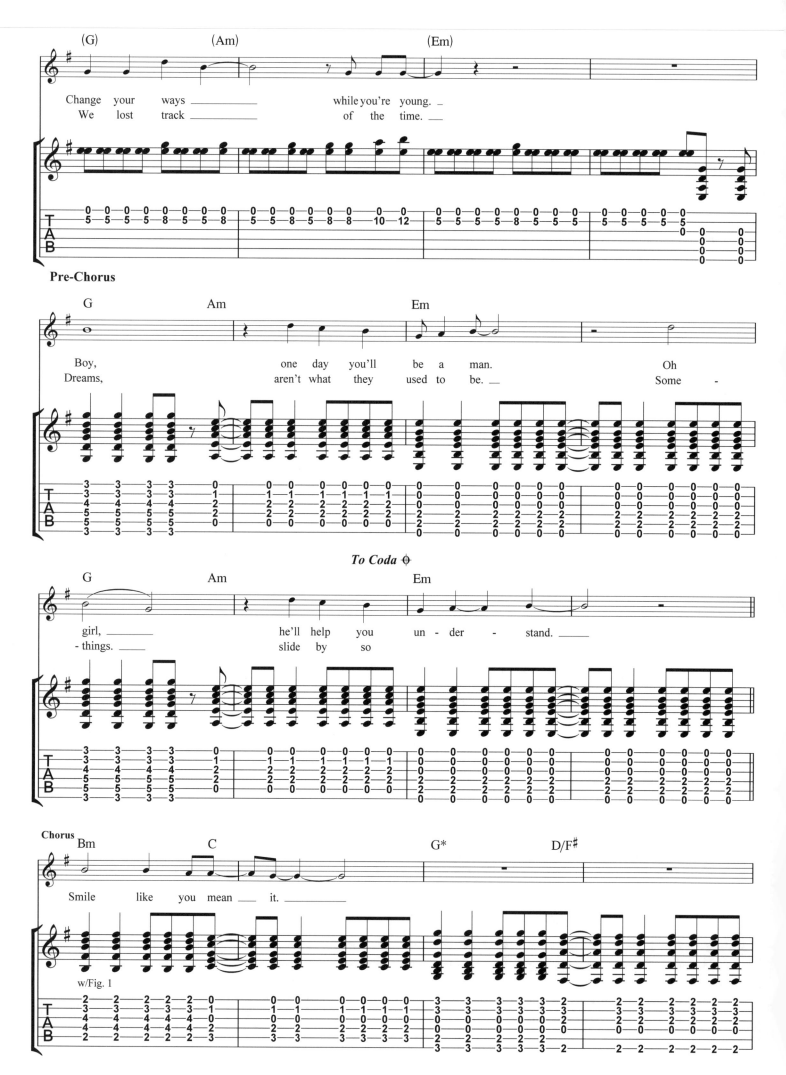

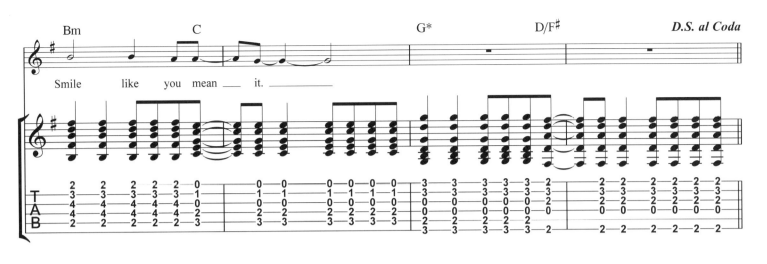

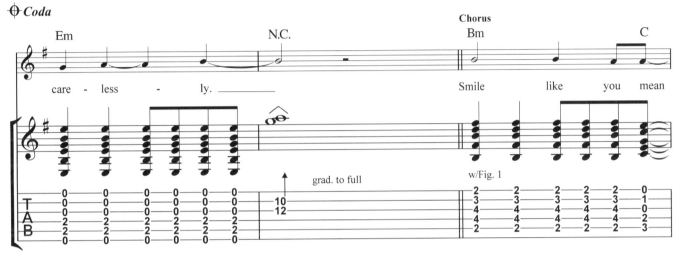

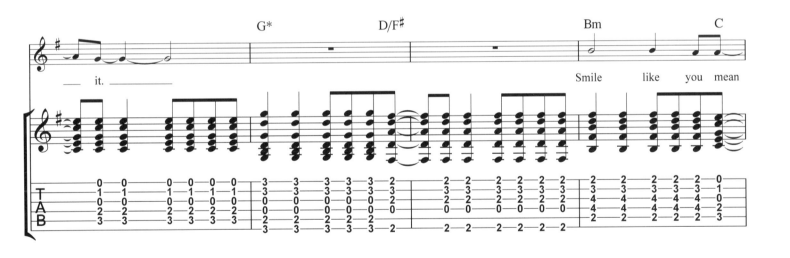

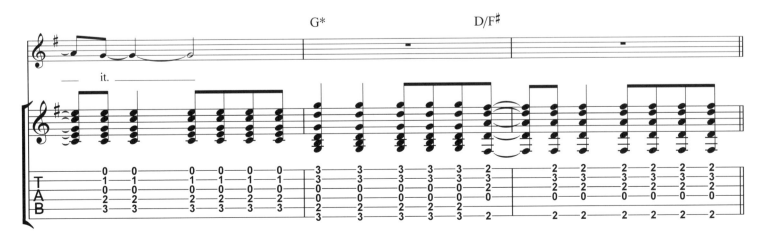

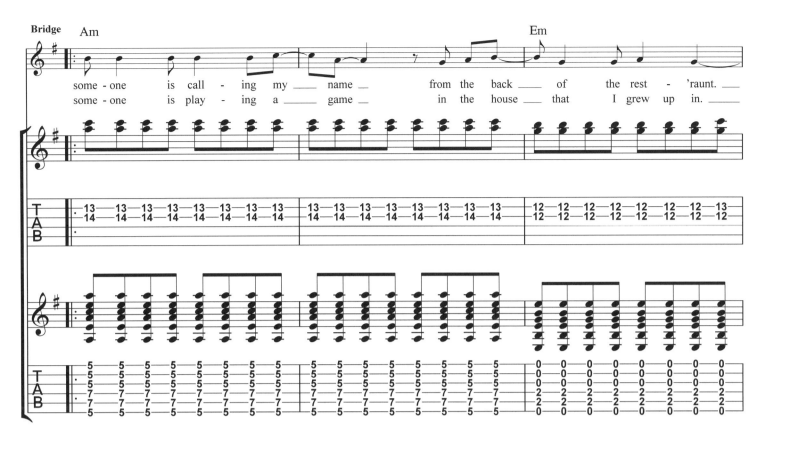

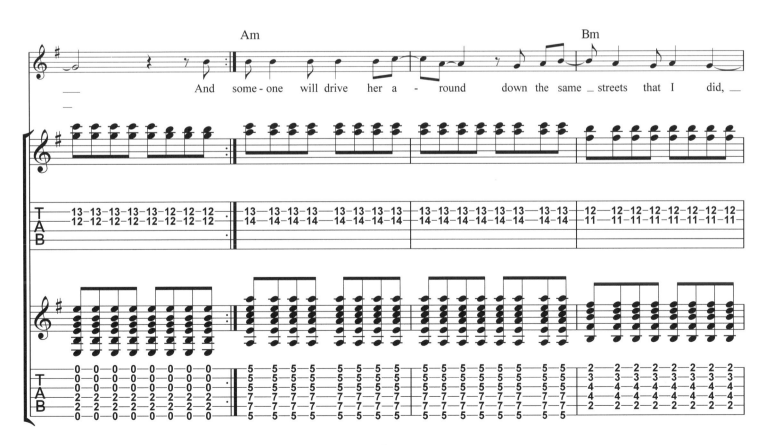

95

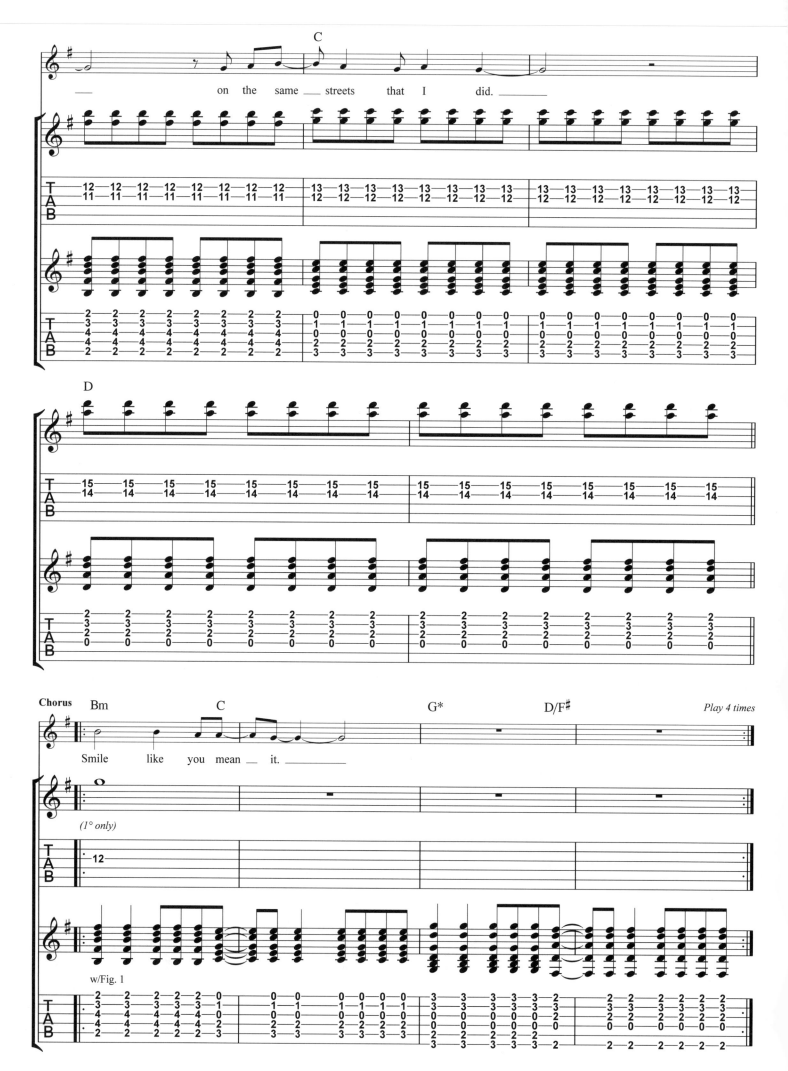

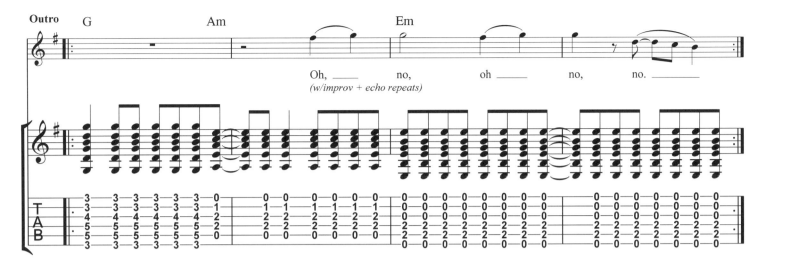

Outro G   Am   Em

Oh, _____ no, oh _____ no, no. _____
(w/improv + echo repeats)

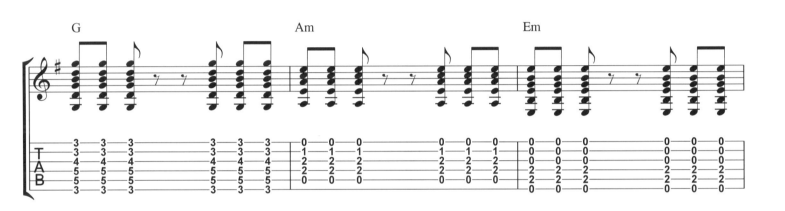

G   Am   Em

Keyboard arr. for Gtr.

G   Am   Em

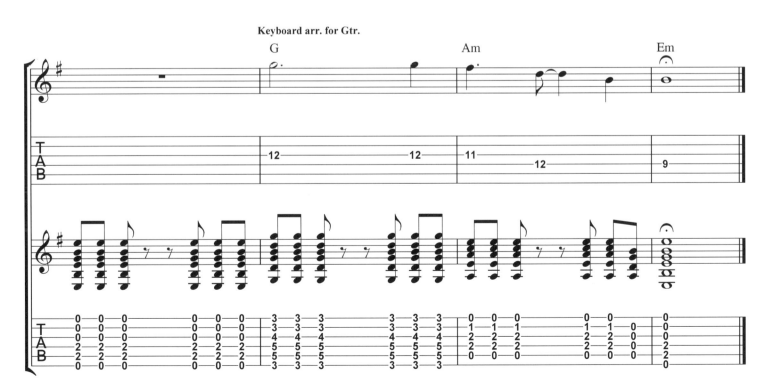

97

Blood

Words & Music by
Thomas Smith, Russell Leetch, Christopher Urbanowicz & Edward Lay

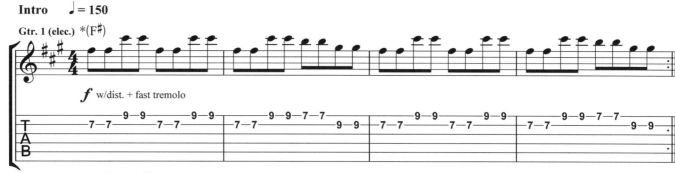

*chords implied by harmony

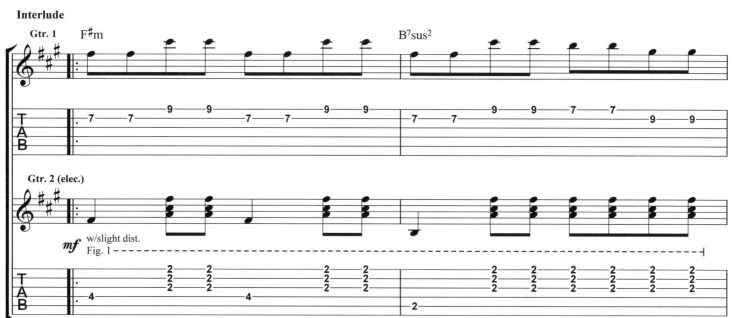

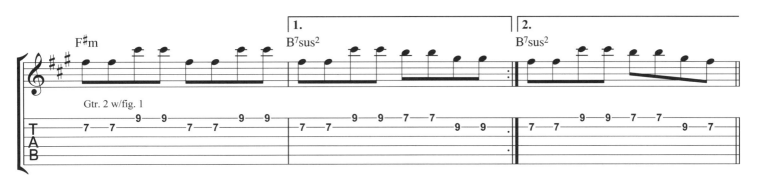

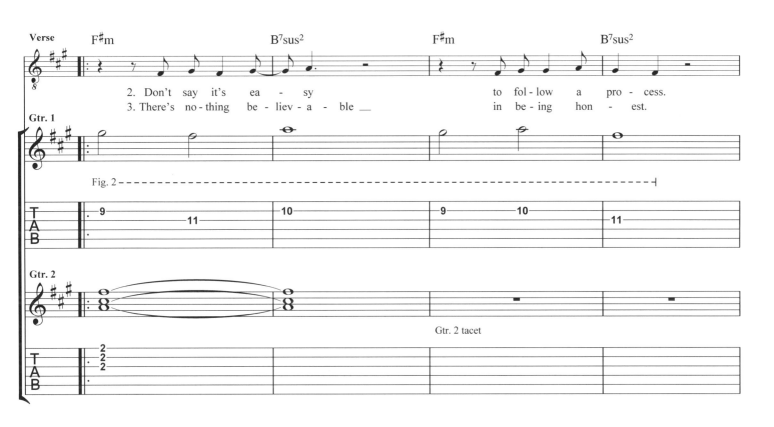

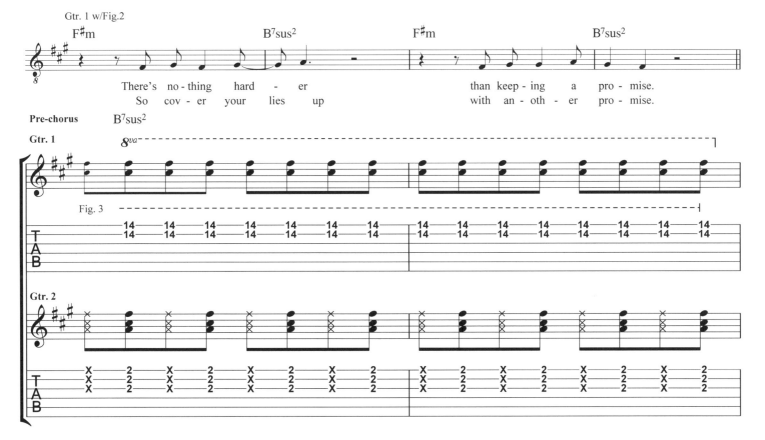

99

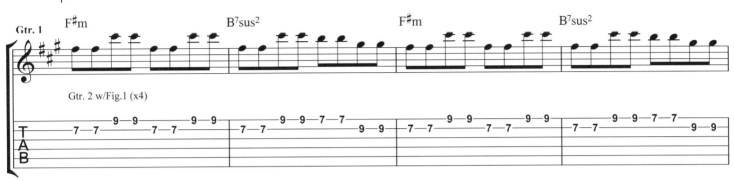

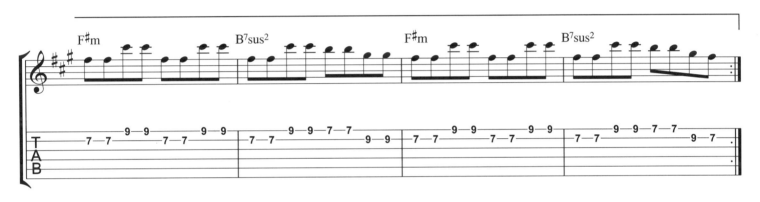

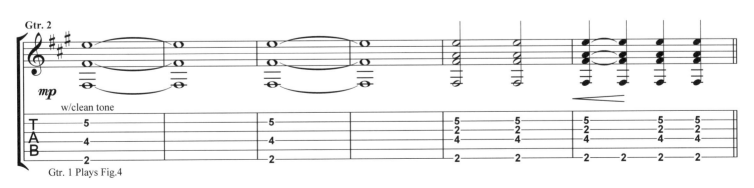

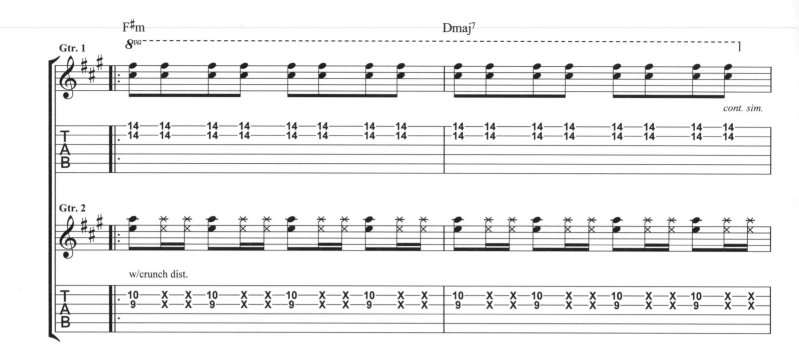

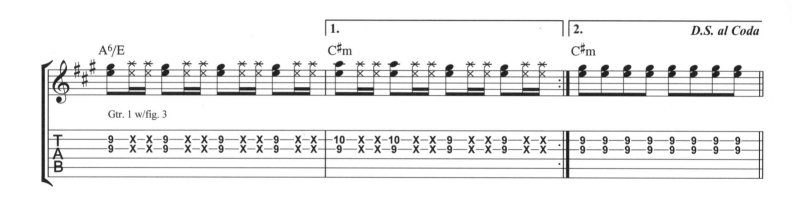

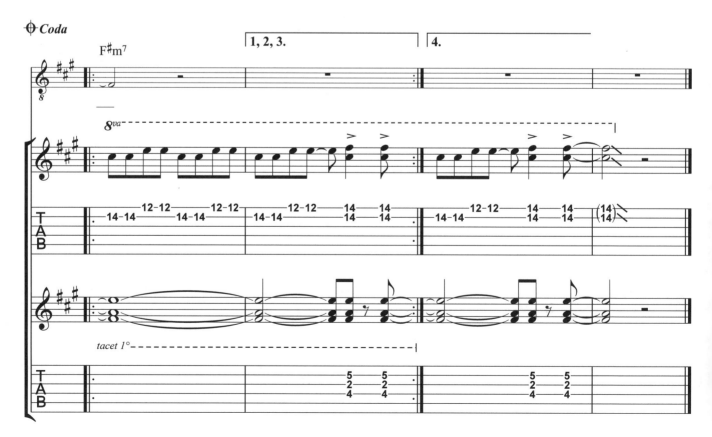

Alive & Amplified

Words & Music by
Phil Ochs, Lauren Christy, Scott Spock, Graham Edwards & Samuel Bounaugurio

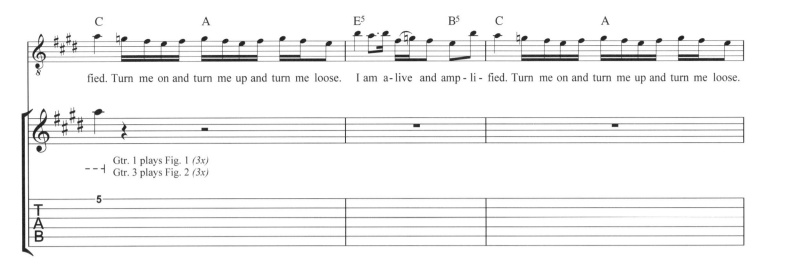

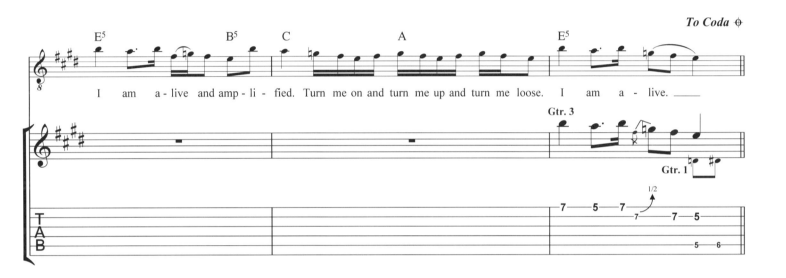

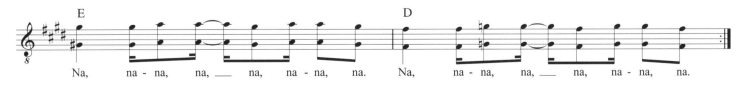

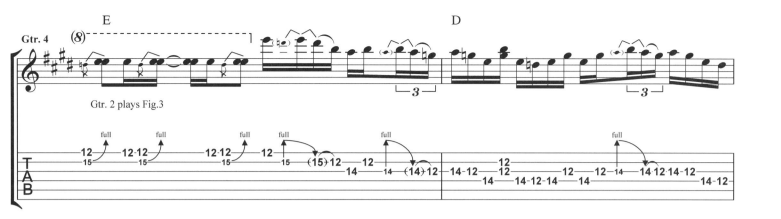

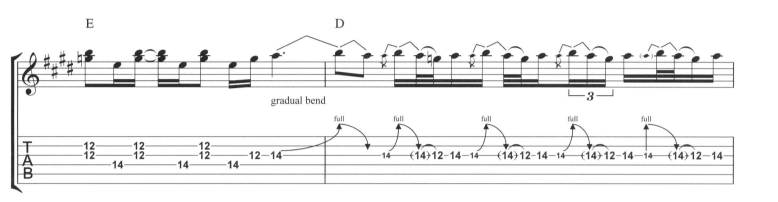

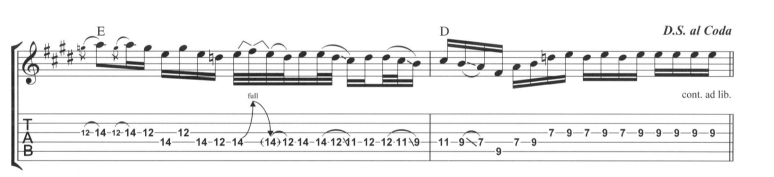

I Like The Way

Words & Music by
Christopher Karyotakis & Dylan Burns

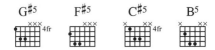

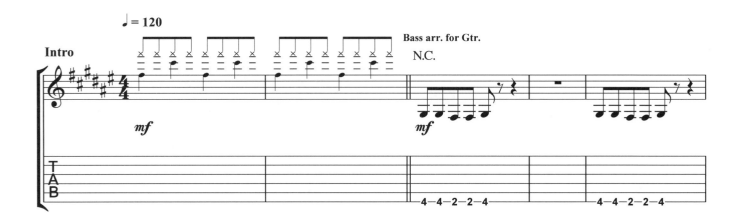

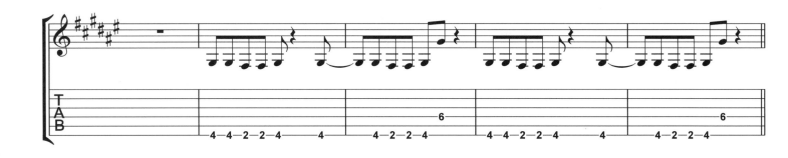

Spoken: There's so ma-ny things I like a-bout you. I just don't know where to

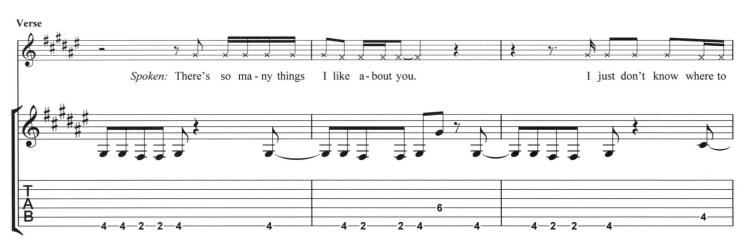

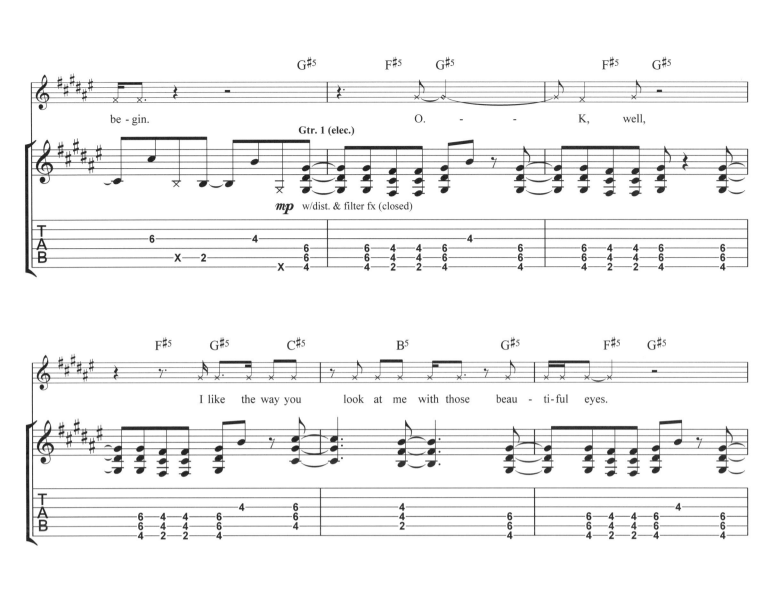

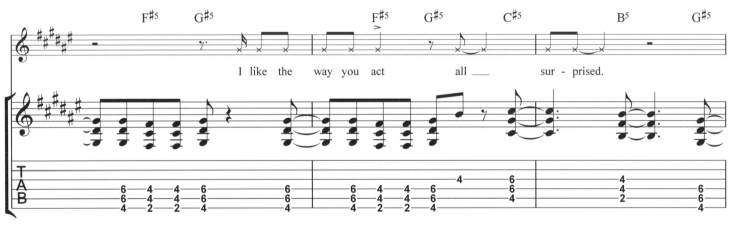

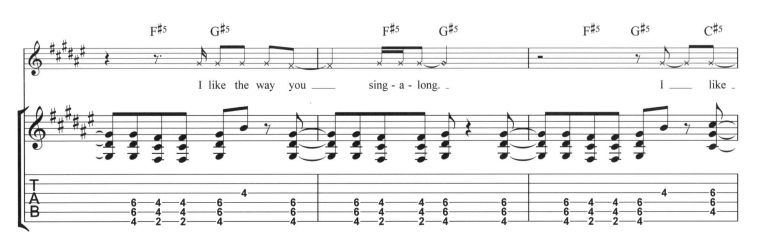

109

the way you, _ al - ways _ get it wrong.

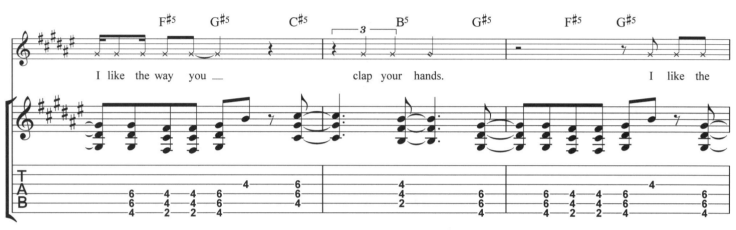

I like the way you _ clap your hands. I like the

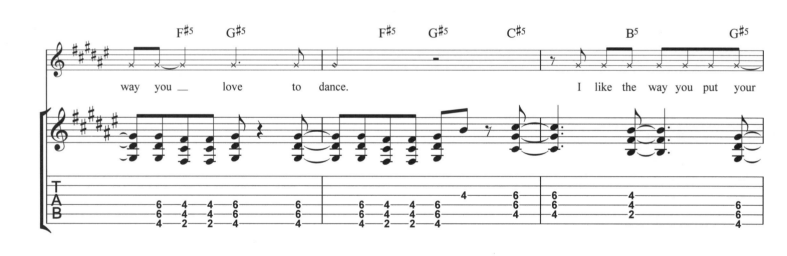

way you _ love to dance. I like the way you put your

_ hands up in the air. _ I like the way you _____ shake your

111

(Vocal on D.S. only)

Kybd. arr. for Gtr.

112

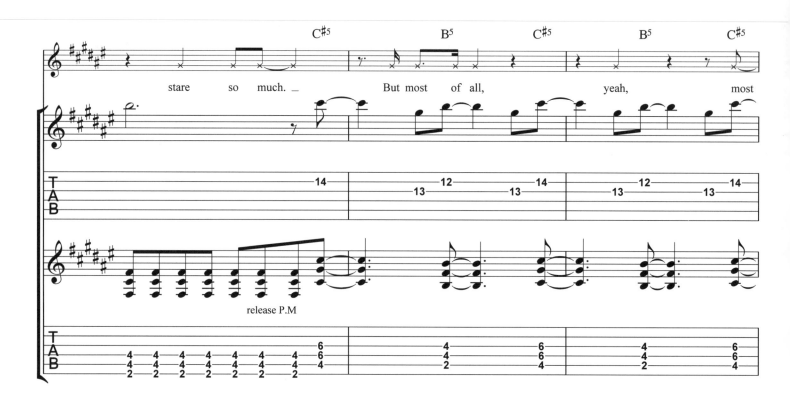

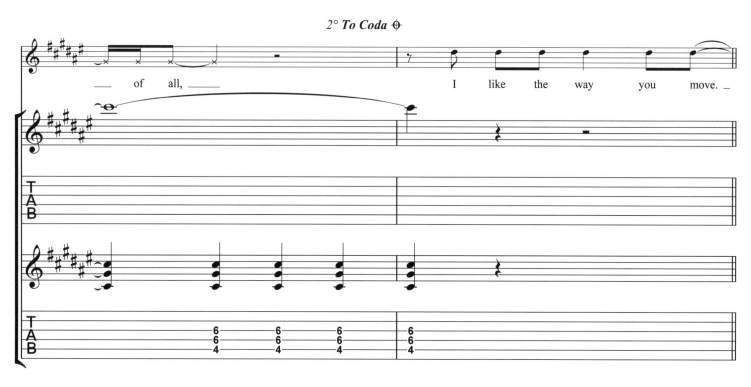

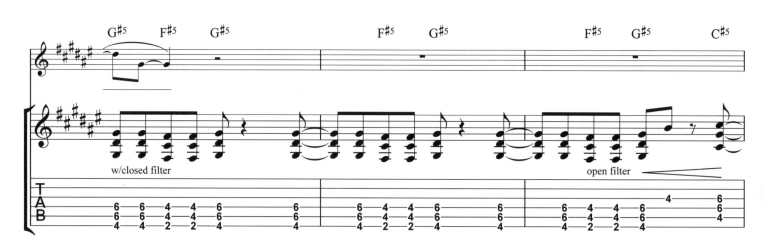

I like the way you move.

I like the way you move.

Girl

Words & Music by
Beck Hansen, Michael Simpson & John King

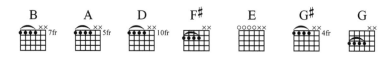

To match recording tune all strings down one semitone

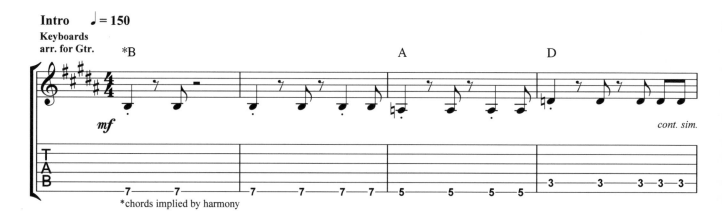

*chords implied by harmony

1. And I saw her, yeah, I saw her with the black tongue tied, wear-ing ros-es.
2. And I saw her, yeah, I saw her with her hands tied back, her rags are burn-ing.

With a noose she could hang from the sun, __ and put it out with the dark sun-glass-es.
Throw a coin in the foun-tain of dust, __ white noise, her ears are ring-ing.

Fig. 2

Gtr. 1 plays Fig. 2

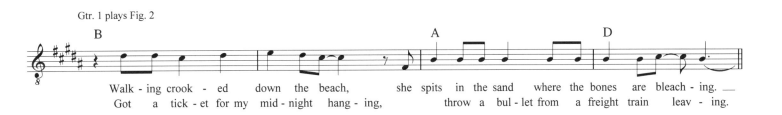

Walk-ing crook-ed down the beach, she spits in the sand where the bones are bleach-ing. __
Got a tick-et for my mid-night hang-ing, throw a bul-let from a freight train leav-ing.

Pre-chorus

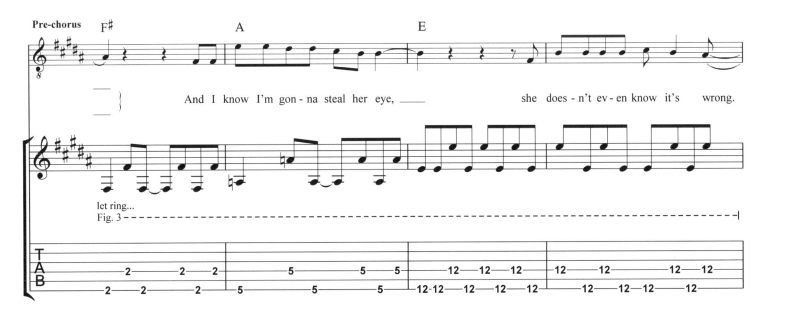

And I know I'm gon-na steal her eye, _____ she does-n't ev-en know it's wrong.

let ring...
Fig. 3

Gtr. 1 plays Fig. 3 (x 1 1/2)

_____ And I know I'm gon-na make her die, _____ and

117

take her where her soul be - longs. _____ I know I'm gon - na steal her eye,

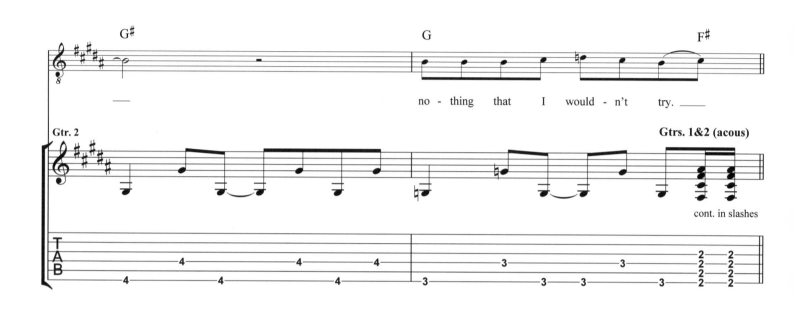

no - thing that I would - n't try. _____

Gtr. 2

Gtrs. 1&2 (acous)

cont. in slashes

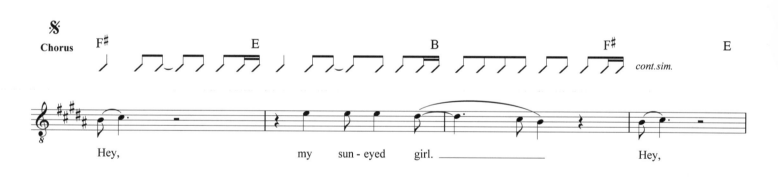

Chorus

cont.sim.

Hey, my sun - eyed girl. _____ Hey,

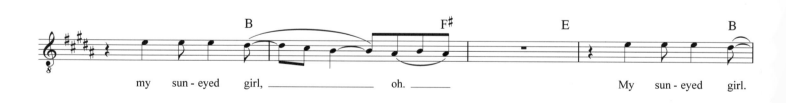

my sun - eyed girl, _____ oh. _____ My sun - eyed girl.

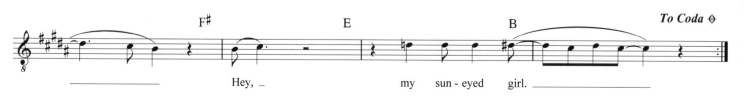

_____ Hey, _ my sun - eyed girl. _____

118

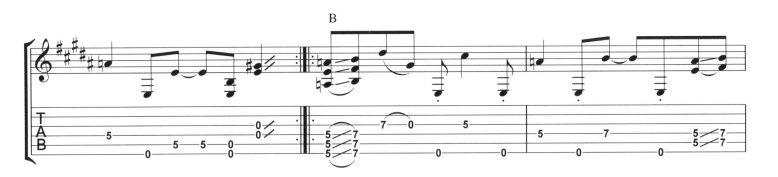

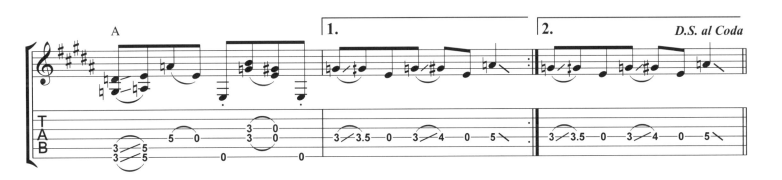

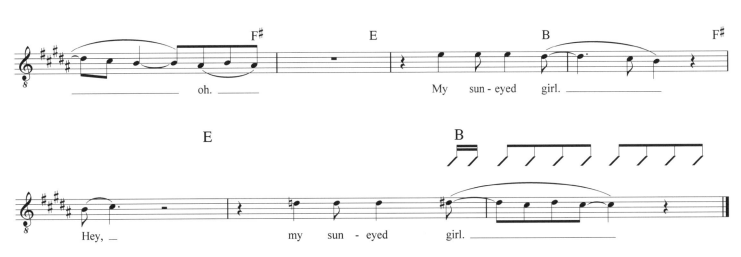

119

From The Floorboards Up

Words & Music by
Paul Weller

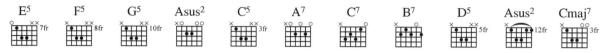

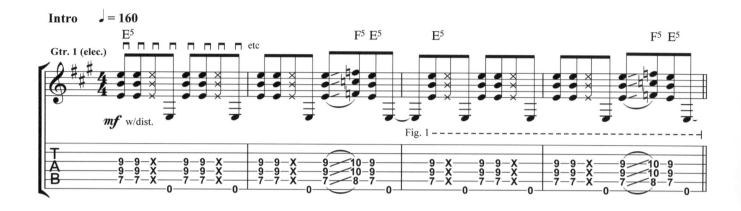

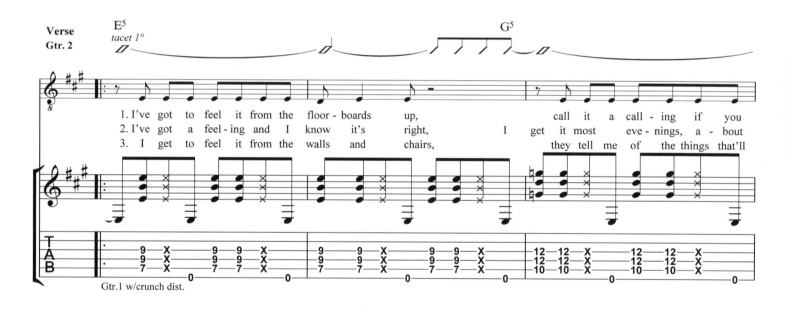

1. I've got to feel it from the floor-boards up, call it a call-ing if you
2. I've got a feel-ing and I know it's right, I get it most eve-nings, a-bout
3. I get to feel it from the walls and chairs, they tell me of the things that'll

like that touch. __ Call it what you will, I real-ly don't care too much. __
ev-'ry night. __ The scenes in the air, __ daz-zles like can-dle light. __
al-ways be there. All that is not, __ will have to go back to dust. __

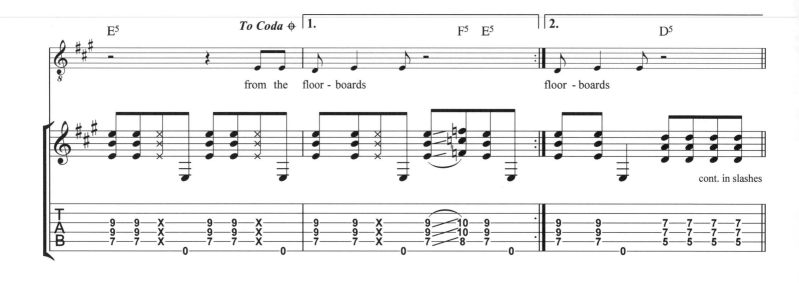

from the floor - boards

floor - boards

cont. in slashes

Gtr. solo

Gtr. 3 (elec.)

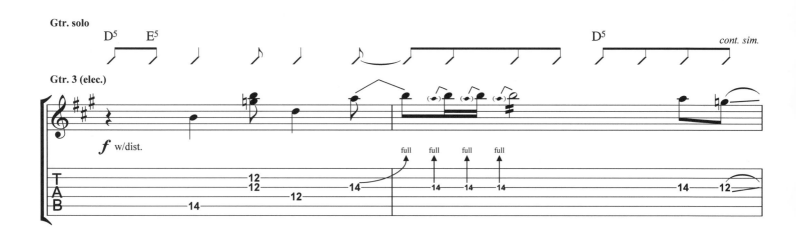

f w/dist.

full   full   full   full

Gtr. 1 w/Fig.1

cont. sim.

Gtr. 1 w/Fig.1

cont. sim.

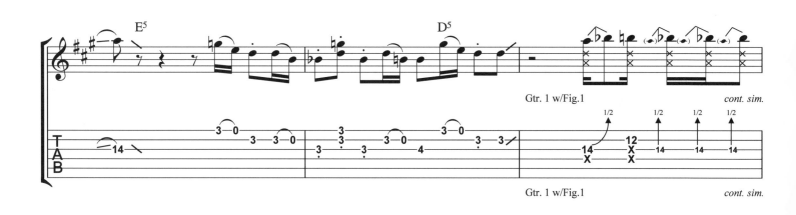

gradual bend
Gtr. 1 w/Fig. 1

1/2   full

full

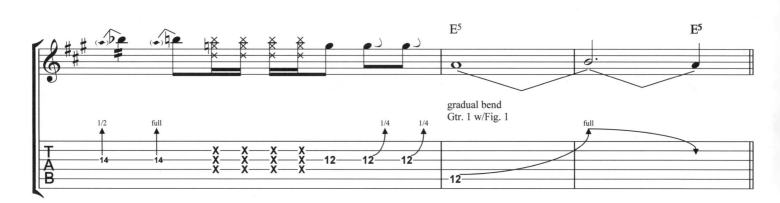

Devil

Words & Music by
Kelly Jones

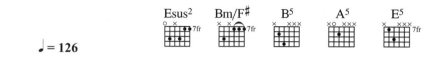

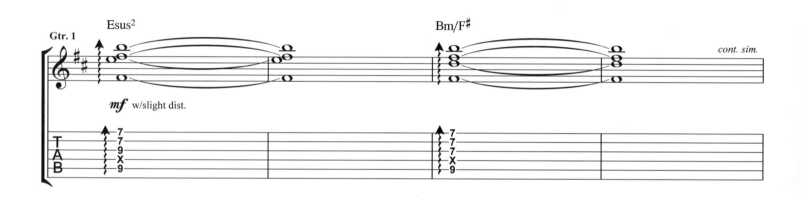

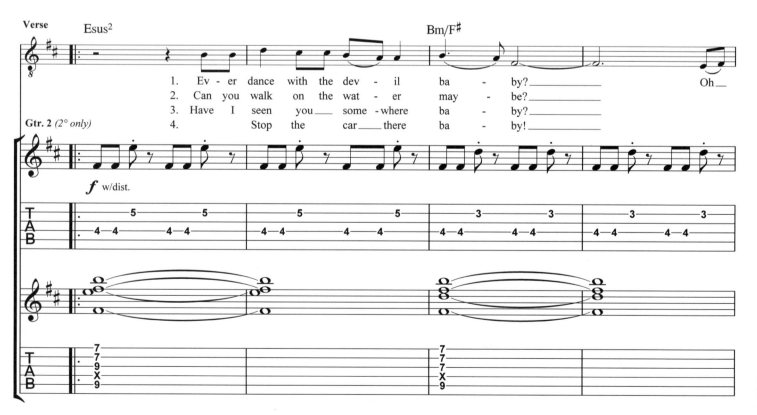

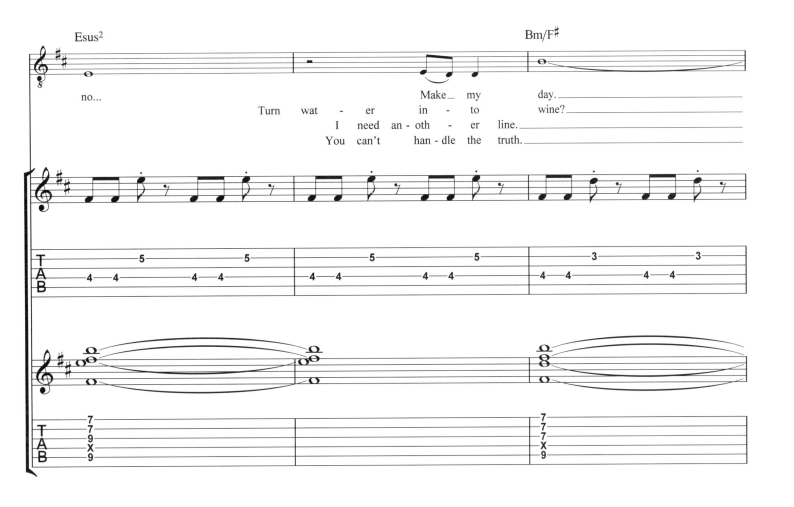

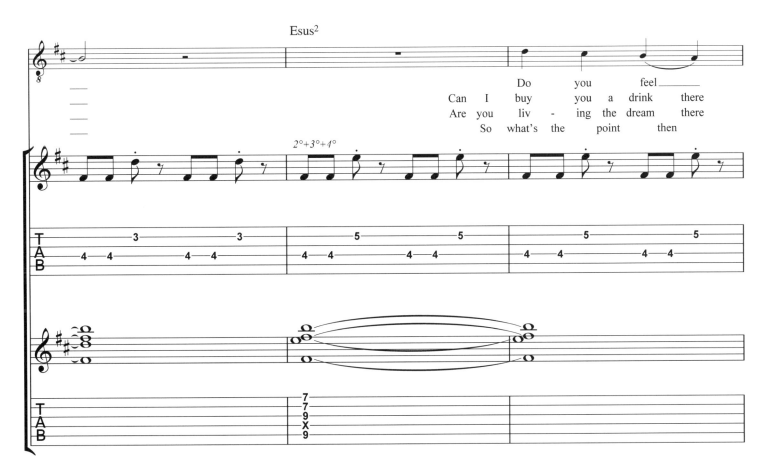

125

King Of The Rodeo

Words & Music by
Caleb Followill, Jared Followill, Matthew Followill & Ivan Followill

*chords implied by harmony

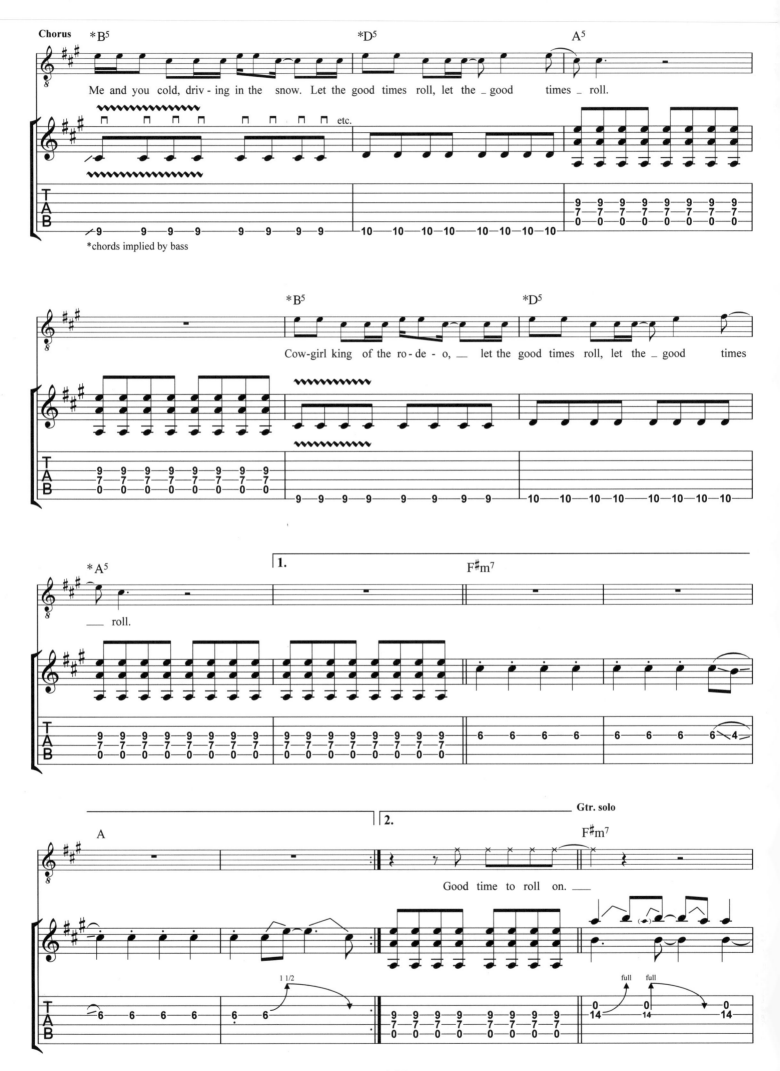

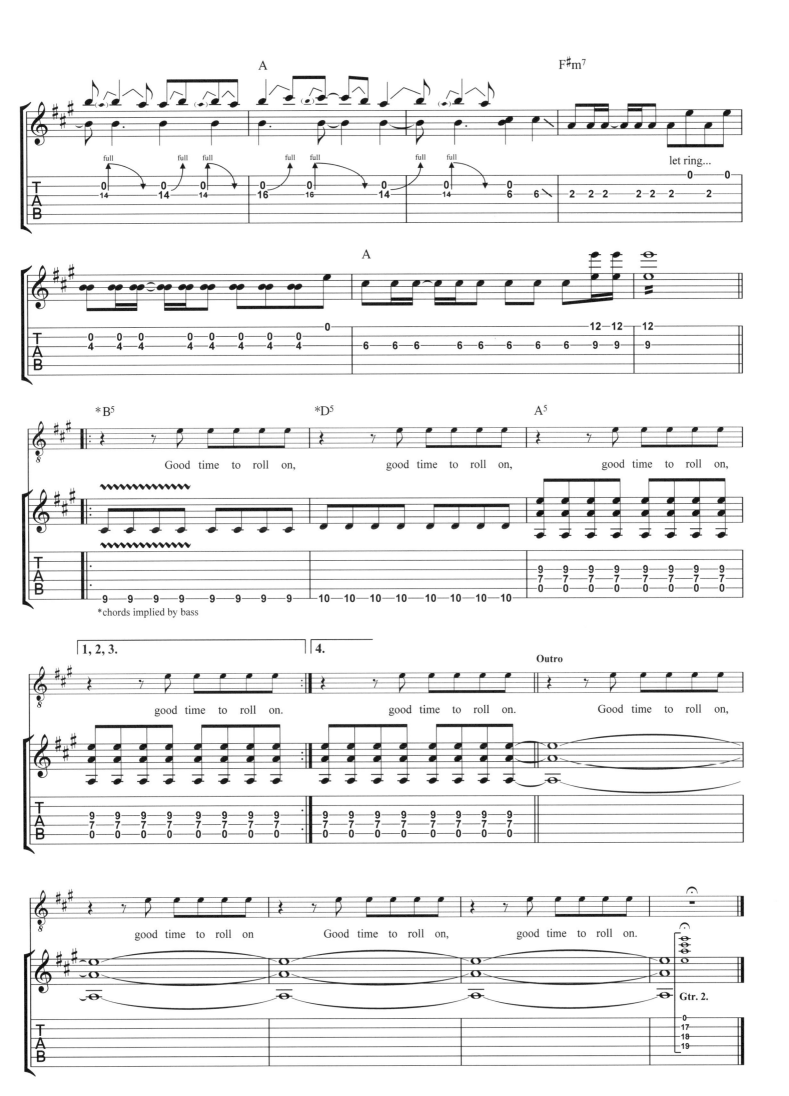

Good time to roll on, good time to roll on, good time to roll on,

*chords implied by bass

good time to roll on. good time to roll on. Good time to roll on,

good time to roll on Good time to roll on, good time to roll on.

Finding Out True Love Is Blind

Words & Music by
Brian Karscig & Jason Hill

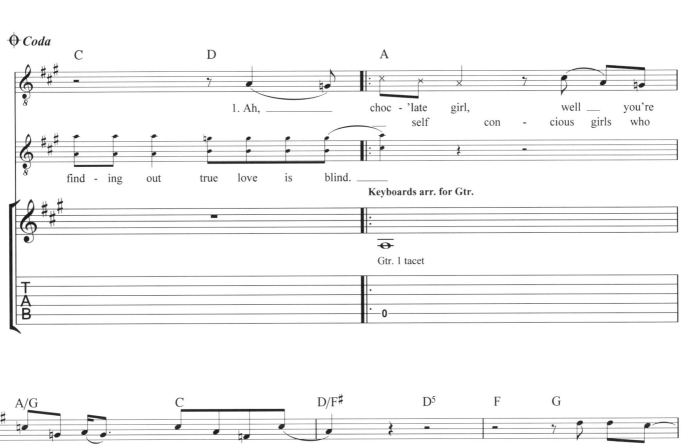

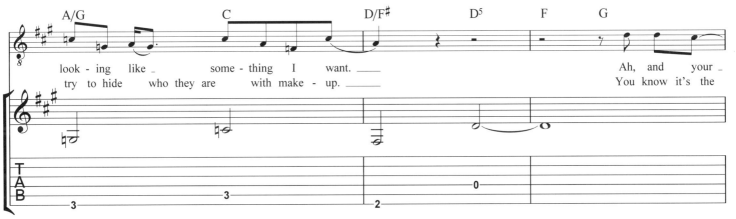

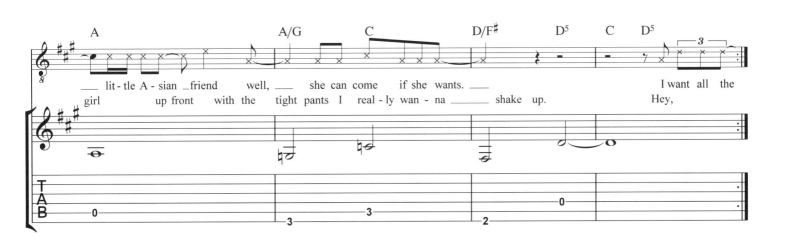

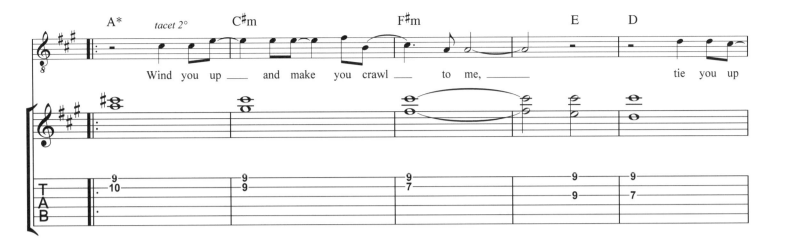

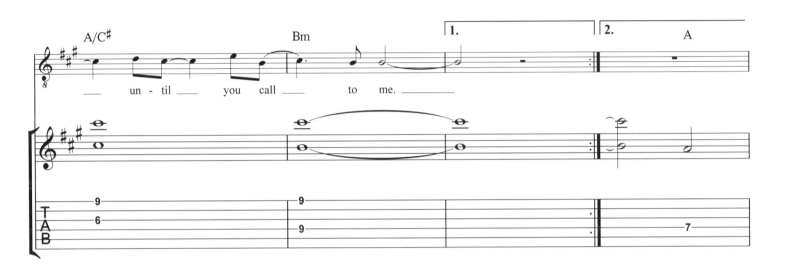

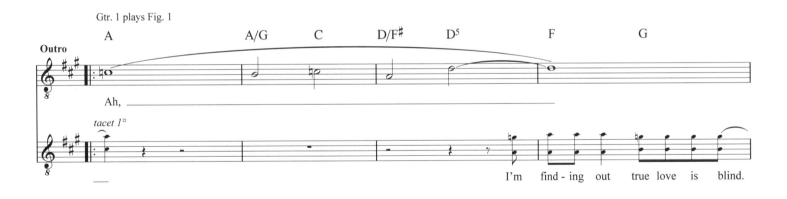

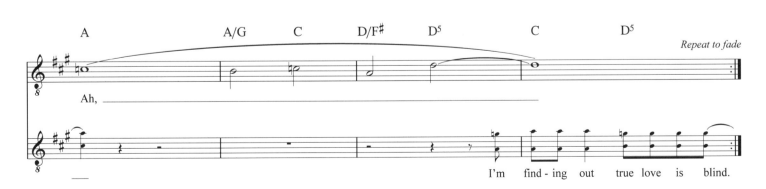

139

Smoke It

Words & Music by
Courtney Taylor-Taylor & Miles Zuniga

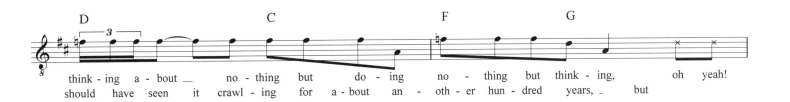

think - ing a - bout ___ no - thing but do - ing no - thing but think - ing, oh yeah!
should have seen it crawl - ing for a - bout an - oth - er hun - dred years, _ but

I know what it is ____ to be there. Now peo - ple,
I nev - er want - ed it ____ to be there _ no. A - li - mo - ny, pa - li - mo - ny, don't

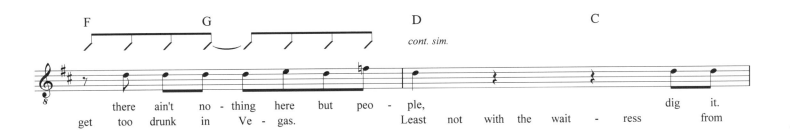

there ain't no - thing here but peo - ple, dig it.
get too drunk in Ve - gas. Least not with the wait - ress from

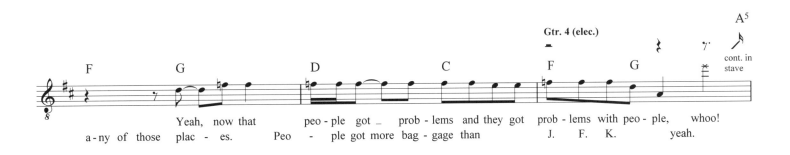

Yeah, now that peo - ple got _ prob - lems and they got prob - lems with peo - ple, whoo!
a - ny of those plac - es. Peo - ple got more bag - gage than J. F. K. yeah.

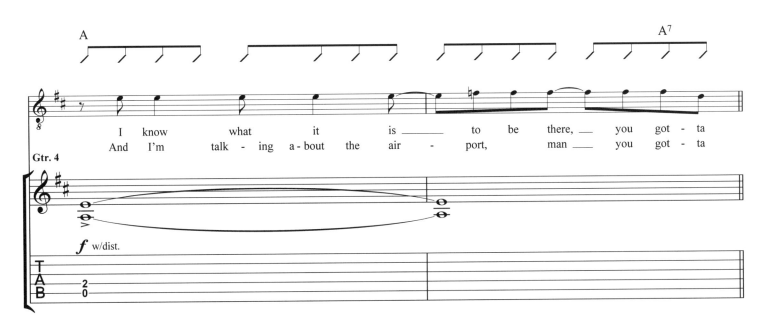

I know what it is ____ to be there, _ you got - ta
And I'm talk - ing a - bout the air - port, man ___ you got - ta

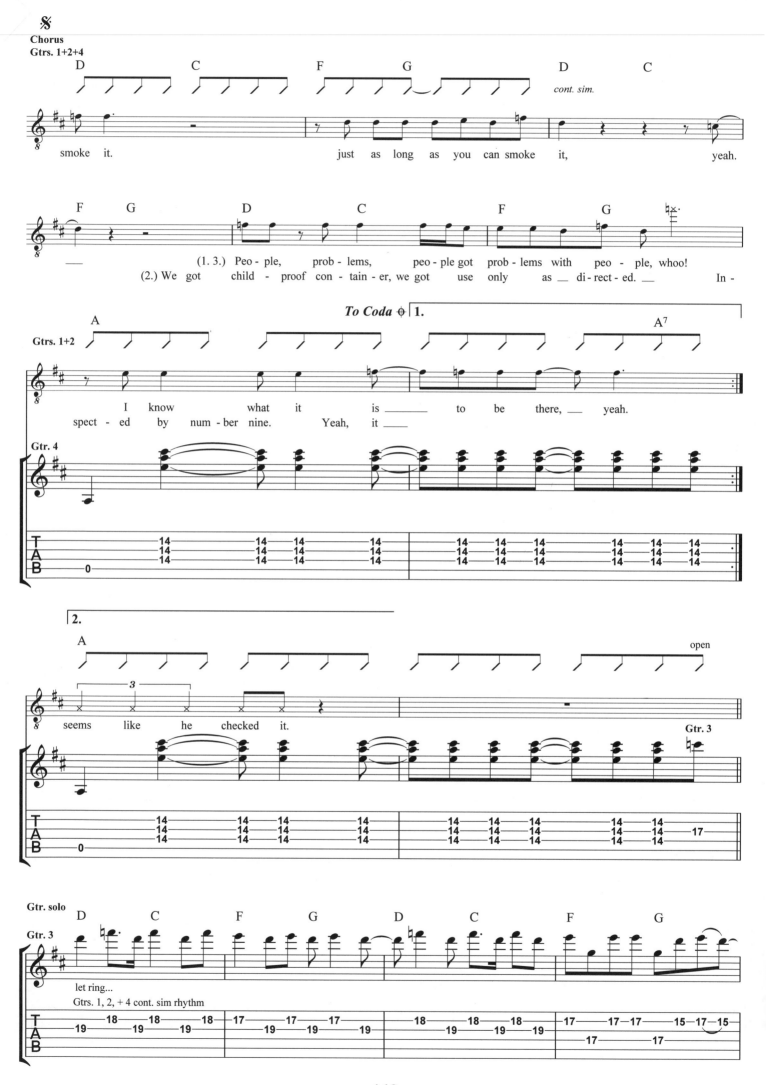

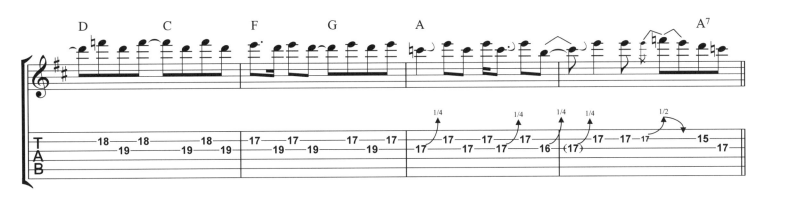

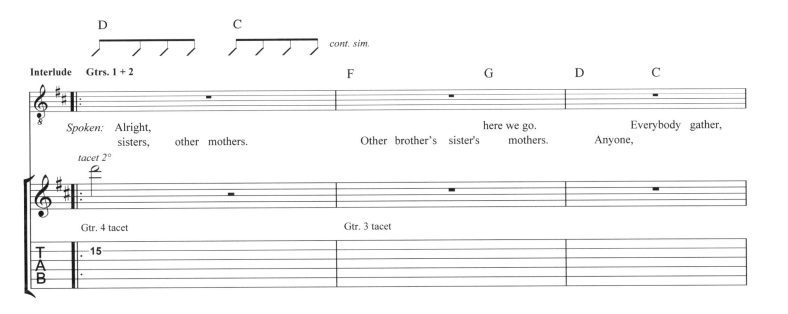

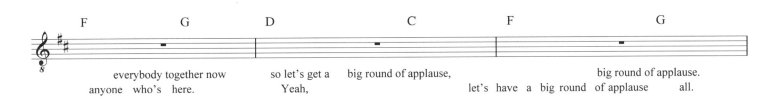

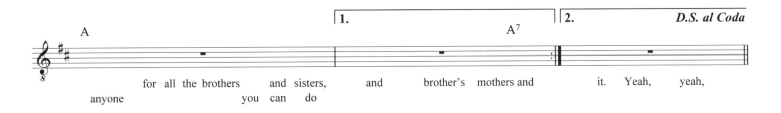

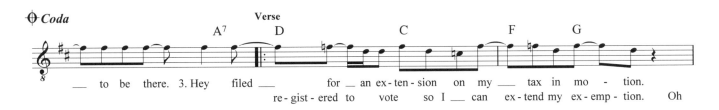

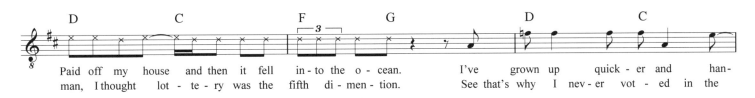

123456789